EATING SECRETS

The Ultimate Guide to Take Control and Overcome Bingeing and Self-Sabotage

KARYN DE MOL & MEGAN HARRIS

WHY NOT HAVE MEGAN HARRIS AND KARYN DE MOL AS GUEST SPEAKERS ON YOUR PODCAST OR AT YOUR NEXT SEMINAR, MEETUP, FESTIVAL OR EVENT?

HOW TO TAKE CONTROL AND OVERCOME BINGEING AND SELF SABOTAGE

Email: support@relationshifters.com
Website: www.relationshifters.com

THE AUTHORS

Karyn de Mol and Megan Harris are both therapists passionate about helping people to have normal relationships with food and their bodies. Qualifications between them include Hypnotherapy, Coaching, Positive Psychology, Neuro Linguistic Programming, Kinesiology, Energy and Body Work. They have a passion for seeing clients thrive after overcoming personal adversity.

This book was written because both women overcame similar histories with bingeing. They now help others conquer the endless cycle of confusion and despair that come with eating battles.

BOOKS BY MEGAN HARRIS & KARYN DE MOL

EATING SECRETS

The Ultimate Guide to Take Control and Overcome Bingeing and Self Sabotage

While most people can relate to overeating on occasions, the lives of people who binge are significantly disrupted by bingeing and the aftermath. If you eat normally while with others, and then secretly binge on food and hide the evidence when you're by yourself, then this is the book you've been looking for.

Eating Secrets helps you understand why it's not your fault and how to start a new chapter. The book offers powerful techniques to take control and overcome self-sabotage and bingeing. This is not a diet book; this is a reclaim your life book.

ONLINE COURSE AND MENTORING BY KARYN DE MOL AND MEGAN HARRIS

How To Control Secret Eating And Bingeing

The strategies, accountability and support you need to take control for good. You don't need to do this alone.

www.relationshifters.com
www.eatingsecrets.com.au/resources

EATING SECRETS

The Ultimate Guide to Take Control and Overcome Bingeing and Self-Sabotage

KARYN DE MOL & MEGAN HARRIS

Mind Potential Publishing
by The Potentialist

Authors: Megan Harris and Karyn de Mol
Title: Eating Secrets
ISBN Paperback: 978-1-922380-18-0
ISBN Kindle: 978-1-922380-20-3

A catalogue record for this book is available from the National Library of Australia

Category: Self Help Techniques I Health

Publisher: Mind Potential Publishing
Division of Mind Design Centre Pty Ltd, PO Box 6094, Maroochydore BC, Queensland, Australia, 4558. International Phone: +61 405 138 567
Australia Phone: 1300 664 544
www.thepotentialist.com I www.relationshifters.com

Cover design by: NGirl Design I www.ngirldesign.com.au

All insights offered are the authors own and are not intended to offend or replace any spiritual beliefs readers may hold. The author respects faith in its many expressions and encourages readers to follow their own beliefs.

LIMITS OF LIABILITY | DISCLAIMER OF WARRANTY:
The authors and publisher of this book have used their best efforts in preparing this material and they disclaim any warranties, (expressed or implied) for any particular purpose. The information presented in this publication is compiled from sources believed to be accurate at the time of printing, however the publisher assumes no responsibility for omissions or errors. The authors and publisher shall not be held liable for any loss or other damages, including, but not limited to incidental, consequential, or any other. This publication is not intended to replace or substitute medical or professional advice, the authors and publisher disclaim any liability, loss or risk incurred as a direct or indirect consequence of the use of any content.

Mind Potential Publishing bears no responsibility for the accuracy of the information provided as either online or offline links contained in this publication. The use of links to websites does not constitute an endorsement by the publisher. The publisher assumes no liability for content or opinion expressed by the authors. Opinions expressed by the authors do not represent the opinion of Mind Potential Publishing or Mind Design Centre Pty Ltd.

Printed in Australia

MEET THE GIRLS

"We've been there,

We Get You and We have the solutions

See you on the inside,
Megan & Karyn xx"

DEDICATION

We dedicate this book to those who have suffered and struggled with their eating secrets and body image issues like we have. You are not alone. It's an awful and painful way to live. That's why we bring you the solutions you'll find in this book.

We also dedicate this book to those on similar journeys, who have shared their hopes, fears and their most secret thoughts, as well as their experiences and ideas, with us. We are deeply grateful to you all.

May this book be the start of your journey to finding peace and self-acceptance.

Megan and Karyn

CONTENTS

FOREWORD

The Missing Link.

When I was asked to write the foreword for Karyn and Megan's book, I knew it was something I had to do.

Eating Secrets is one of those books that you'll wish you'd found years ago. I believe that every weight loss or dieting 'guru' with the latest fad should provide this book as the companion to their diet book because the chance of long-term success would escalate.

The dieting industry rarely provides any skills or emotional support that would help a dieter develop a sustainable relationship with food.

I recommend Eating Secrets to my Unzip readers too! My motto is, '*To change your body permanently, you must also change your mind.*' That is precisely what Eating Secrets is all about. Once you've improved your relationship with food, you empower your relationship with yourself, your mind, and your body.

Let's face it; we all know what we should eat to be healthy, right? We all know what we 'should' do to lose weight, yes?

We've all poured over countless magazines and diet plans: eat this, weigh and measure that, don't do this and don't do that, exercise right, drink more water … you know what to do, I know what to do, but how many of us have the right headspace and habits in place to follow the plan consistently, as a lifestyle?

Even if we manage to change our eating habits initially, the big questions are:

1. Do we have the skills to make the change permanent?
2. Can we overcome the daily cravings, the emotional eating urges, the doubts and fears?
3. Will the tough days that trigger all kinds of old habits, and the great days that trigger the need for reward, win in the end and restart the dieting cycle?

This book provides a bunch of tools and therapeutic strategies for the reader to overcome these challenges. Karyn and Megan understand and know it from the inside. That's what I love about this book and the authors. They are real, they bare all, they are honest, funny and inspiring. They get you; they've heard your secrets whispered inside their heads; they know you because they've been where you are.

Megan and Karyn help the reader understand that it's not their fault they've developed this love/hate/shame relationship with food, and for some, their body too.

The book is packed with simple tips and tactics to help you overcome binge eating for good - it's not about good or bad food choices, it's about being open to feeling your feelings, modifying your behaviour and responses to food and eating.

Maggie Wilde - The Potentialist
Clinical Therapist Dip. CCH, Award-Winning Author & Publisher to the Wellness Industry

STRESS EATING
BINGEIN
HAPPY AND SAD
SHAME

INTRODUCTION

Shhhhh! For a long time, we had a secret.

A secret that we finally feel comfortable to share with you.

Our 'secret' was our unhealthy and toxic relationship with food.

Food! We can't live without it! We have to eat every day in order to live, but, and here's the kicker, if you have an 'unhealthy' relationship with food – you often lose sight of what is 'normal'.

You might go through stages where you binge eat, or when you pull yourself together and the opposite happens—you go through periods of restricting and overcompensating for your 'weakness'.

You find yourself on a roller coaster ride with the 'part of you' that feels like you have no control.

If you suffer from binge eating, it can be a very lonely and secretive world indeed. What we had to face throughout the years that we battled with binge eating and restrictive dieting, is that we didn't always know what a 'normal' relationship with food was. We lost sight of what was normal. There were so many mixed messages about what we should or shouldn't do, that getting off the secret rollercoaster was one very complex challenge we wanted to solve, for our peace of mind and health too.

- When had it become our normal to hoover three family blocks of chocolate after a rough day and hide the wrappers under the rubbish in the bin so no one could see the evidence?
- When had it become normal to squash sadness or loneliness down with bread?

- When had it become normal to binge drink to fit in?
- When did punishing ourselves by starving our body the next day become normal? And…
- When was it that it became normal to constantly beat yourself up and tell yourself you were not worthy of having a healthy body?

As much as we dreamt of the day when food would lose its power over us, the truth was not, *when* did it become normal, that we needed to solve. It was *why* had it become normal? You can't solve a complex challenge with a complex solution. It always comes down to Why, not When.

Binge eating and restricting food or overeating happens *for a reason*. Solve the reason why you do what you do, and you make peace with that action and have power over the outcome.

At this moment in time, you have a specific relationship and lots of rules associated with food and eating.

These are YOUR secrets.

Somehow, you developed a rule that allows food to rule your life. You created have to's, should do's, and must or must not do's associated with food, and the truth is, you need to throw the rule book out.

In times of stress, we all experience different feelings and moments of boredom, periods of loneliness, anxiety and uncertainty. During this time, if your first impulse is to reach for your favourite comfort food, you've fallen into the same trap that we did. We found comfort and distraction by binge eating.

Using food as a decoy to manage the 'stuff' of life, that you didn't know how to manage at the time, becomes a habit, a fallback pattern. At some point that pattern becomes the way to handle 'stuff'. It becomes normal for your brain to trigger the same urges and reactions to those stressors. No matter how much part of you wants to change that pattern, the part of your brain that has learned it, fights with you to keep it.

This book teaches you to become curious about those patterns. To ponder objectively the habits, cravings and 'go-to' foods, and to see them as insights into understanding what makes you tick. These are openings into learning more about yourself, your strengths, weaknesses and ability to willingly change, once you know how.

As the authors of Eating Secrets, we will explain a fundamental truth that will set you free!

"Trying to make yourself feel better and feeling better about yourself are two very different things!" Megan and Karyn

This book came about because we both had to overcome our individual 'secrets' with food. Like anyone with a secret shame, our relationship with food caused us both years of exhausting stress.

Just like you, we've spent years trying to find answers. In preparation for publishing this book we sat down and interviewed each other about our journey with food and eating… here's a little of how it came together…

Megan:

It was more than our challenges with food that brought us together, we were both studying to gain formal qualifications as clinical therapists. We had similar backgrounds and beliefs and when we opened up to each other, we discovered we also shared this huge secret.

Karyn:

Our secret agony, which we had never really spoken of to anyone, nor honestly acknowledged to ourselves at that time, was that we'd both spent years thinking we 'weren't good enough' and 'something was wrong with us'.

Megan:

We'd stuffed down those feelings for years, certain, until we met, that we were the odd ones out. Karyn's way to stuff those feelings down was to binge eat; mine was restrictive eating and binge drinking.

Karyn:

Our headspace was filled with worries and doubt, if only we were the right size or had the perfect shape, surely, we would be happy then.

We spent years bereft of motivation, suffering crippling shame and emotional stress. We gained and lost a lot of weight, then rinsed and repeated the cycle again. I remember when we first met and bravely talked about our 'secrets', it felt like a relief to talk about the burden with someone who understood.

Megan:

We had both spent so much time awake in the middle of the night, wondering why we weren't happy and why we did the things we did. Depending on the mood our 'best friends' were either chocolate bars, Doritos or wine, and although very destructive, it was how we dealt with 'stuff'.

Karyn:

Once we started to feel more at peace, once we had strategies and strength to start helping ourselves, we were both determined that we were going to help as many people as we could who were suffering in silence too.

Megan:

We know what it's like when you're trying your hardest to hold it together. Both of us have lived a life where food became both a friend and a dreaded enemy. We understand how it feels to punish yourself with food one day and reward yourself the next. We hope that our stories presented throughout this book, and our honesty about the good and the bad, help you realise that you are understood too.

Karyn:

Even more than that, we hope that the strategies and techniques we step you through in this book, give you breathing space and hope that there is a way to feel more peaceful. There are ways to move toward a healthier relationship with yourself, food and your body.

Megan:

Our aim with this book is to show you that it is possible to live a life where food does not consume your every waking thought. That you can start to believe you are worthy.

Karyn:

To learn that self-love and self-acceptance are the keys that will prevent you from turning to food or alcohol or any other substance to satisfy your appetite for love.

Megan:

In hindsight, both of us used food to regulate happiness. We had asked ourselves a thousand times why we were unhappy and never knew the answer. We both had good jobs, on the surface no one would ever have known what we were 'stuffing down'. But we would slink away to our secret stash, and then beat ourselves up for doing it again and again.

Karyn:

Looking back, we were very committed to feeling depressed and broken. Our emotions were literally eating us from within, and because we didn't know how to deal with those emotions, we ate more to suppress them.

Whether you are ready to stop binge eating, or ready to take baby steps to learn how to safely move away from those emotions instead of swallowing them down, then this book has the strategies to help. It has the systems to take back control and find an inner peace with yourself and food.

Megan:

For me it started as a symptom of something much, much bigger, something that I didn't want to face, and looking back, didn't really know how to face at the time.

Our aim is that you will also feel a connection throughout the book, knowing that Karyn and I have been there too, and we have your back. When you feel understood, that someone has taken the steps before you, then we can hold your hand and guide you one step at a time to get you where you want to be too.

Karyn:

Our hope is that you'll let us show you how to safely face whatever needs to be faced to get you where you want to be too.

Megan:

One step at a time, one choice, and one small win at a time. This book teaches you how to achieve those small wins and to be proud of them, they are critical for your long-term success.

Karyn and Megan:
Our purpose is to help you shift your relationship with food, and yourself, and to make that shift permanent. Ours has been a tough journey, but we wouldn't be the people we are today if we didn't go through it and come out the other side. Our hope is that by sharing our story – and our secrets – and taking you on this journey, we will help you realise that you are not alone. You no longer need to suffer in secret. You'll realise that what you feel is normal, you're normal and you are okay.

Eating Secrets is the ultimate guide to take control and overcome bingeing and self-sabotage. This is a 'reclaim' your life book. Welcome to the rest of your life!

We've been there. We get you. We have the solutions.

And so can you.

Karyn and Megan

SHHH...

CHAPTER 1
What's Eating You

"I am trying to find myself. Sometimes that's not easy."
Marilyn Monroe

I don't know how I let it get this far.

I would describe it as being stuck in a cyclone, being violently thrown around, completely out of control. Trying to seek answers to questions with no way of knowing where to look or go. Being caught in a dark place, in a prison in my head like being stuck in solitary confinement. I feel isolated, lonely, and alone and trapped by this secret. I have no freedom from it, it's always there. I feel overwhelmed, powerless and out of control.

I feel the heavy burden, the struggle and confusion of not knowing what to do. I'm drained and sick of pretending that all is well. I've been wearing the fake bravado mask, pretending to be in control and happy. Inside I'm spinning wildly out of control.

My mind is torn, I want to escape from the urges and cravings, but I need food to survive.

The more I binge or hide the evidence of eating, the more I feel like a failure.

I don't want to go out, I want to hide.

I feel ashamed.

What is wrong with me?

I'm confused, why do I keep doing this, repeating this cycle?

Am I doing it to try and protect me, or punish myself somehow?

Am I avoiding stuff?

How did I let it get this far?

I feel equally safe and in danger at the same time.

I need to manage the whirlwind of emotions that makes my head spin.

I tell myself I won't eat junk food, but the more I say that, the more I hear food calling me.

I don't know what I've done to become a prisoner to food; but I seem to be serving a very long sentence.

How do I get out of here?

These comments are only some of the exhausting head-battle conversations we've heard our clients say over the years. The thing is, many of these comments have filled our heads too. We get it, the confusion, the regret, the promises, and the self-recrimination are just some of the things we've said to ourselves as well. Our secret lives of binge eating, binge drinking and restrictive dieting were reminiscent of a very messy affair between food, alcohol, starvation and emotions.

→ Secret behaviour
→ Secret pleasure
→ Secret fear
→ Secret choices
→ Secret emotions
→ Secret promises and of course, the secret shame.

The Secret Shame – how did you get here?

The purpose of this book is to safely and privately reveal to yourself the secret beliefs, patterns and emotions you've formed over the years to get you to where you are today.

Here's the thing: you can't change what you don't acknowledge.

Once you safely acknowledge what has been happening, and acknowledge what you're willing to do about it, you can then begin to build a healthier relationship with food and yourself.

We're here to help you access and release the secret stuff you've got going on, deep in your mind, that you may or may not be aware of, that stops you from being the best version of you.

We're here to help you achieve the level of change that you want in your relationship with food and the eating secrets you've harbored so far.

This book provides the secret code to access those secrets, process them and let them go. The information and support you'll find in this book will set you free to step away from the fridge, away from the pantry and have a loving and respectful relationship with food, your body and you. This is not a diet program, but a long-term solution.

Why is the secret so important?

For your brain, the point of binge eating isn't always about the food, it's often not the quantity either. It's the satisfaction of the secret itself.

You eat secretly and you keep it secret, and at first your brain helps you feel good about that. It's not necessarily the eating itself, it's the pleasure of that eating being a secret. Most secret eaters and bingers feel upset by the bingeing once the endorphin rush of the 'hunt' is over. Often, they feel so embarrassed that seeking help seems too hard. There's the shame, hiding and pretending it's all okay. Close friends and family may not even know you binge, and if you gain weight, they often wouldn't dream it was because you binge eat. Often the binger is in denial about the quantity consumed. **Being a binge eater is as lonely as it is serious.**

If you do suffer from a weight problem, you can relate when we say that we have been ridiculed, shamed and faced some harsh critics – most often by people who have never had a weight problem.

As a society, we don't talk about it. It's deemed to be a mental illness or a poor lifestyle choice, or it gets trivialised. The 'fat shaming' and weight stigma contribute to the neglect of the disorder.

We often hear that a 'binger' can be cured by:

- Willpower
- Making better food choices
- Learning about correct portion sizes or starting a balanced diet.

We also hear judgements like:

- It's not a real condition or
- It's a 'choice' to do it, just get on with changing the habit

Eating disorders are not a lifestyle choice or a cry for attention.

Getting help can feel very threatening. Most doctors won't ask about eating behaviours, especially if their patient is of a normal weight. If they did ask – would you tell them anyway?

Whether you binge on food, drink, other substances or a combination, it's a way of dealing with uncomfortable or negative emotions. It's a way to numb the feelings or unhelpful thought patterns. Throughout this book we will deal with the inner struggle associated with binge eating, emotional eating and stress eating, as well as the weight issues associated with that behaviour. We understand these issues because we both have had to deal with them throughout our lives.

One of the greatest gifts we learned to give to ourselves, and hope to share with you, is that you can be free of the shame and the guilt. You can be free of the internal battle that overwhelms you, stresses you and often triggers another layer of emotional eating just to numb out the guilt or shame.

The key to success is this: keep no more secrets about your eating habits. One of the reasons it controls you is because you keep it secret. That doesn't mean you have to shout it from the rooftops, what it means is being honest with yourself, honest with us (the ones who 'get' you, more than you know), honest about it all. We can't change what we don't face, so we start with what's real and what is the truth right now.

Binge Eating is NOT about the food.

Bingers eat to meet a need that has nothing to do with genuine appetite. The need can stem from a subconscious urge for comfort, to self-soothe, to regulate mood and as a coping mechanism for uncomfortable feelings.

This urge for comfort can be described like surfing. You feel the tension build as you are paddling out; fighting the incoming waves of emotions as you paddle to get out to the back of the waves. These emotions are where you believe you can't cope, and something has happened to cause the urge to binge. You finally find yourself out the back at the set of waves. You see the perfect wave coming, so you paddle to jump on it and get swept up in the bingeing, feeling euphoric and excited as you eat your favourite foods. But then comes the wipeout where you feel shame and disgust with yourself. You crash.

To overcome binge eating, start with the 'WHY' you're doing it in the first place.

You can download free resources at

www.eatingsecrets.com.au/resources

Binge eating is different to the occasional overindulgence or 'overeating'.

While most people can relate to overeating on occasions, the lives of people who binge are significantly disrupted by both the binge and the aftermath. Episodes of bingeing are often followed by crippling and overwhelming feelings of distress, shame, guilt, disgust and confusion. Sometimes there's anger that they did it, and helplessness because they 'secretly' know they will do it again.

Unlike those with bulimia nervosa, a person with binge eating disorder will not use compensatory behaviours, such as self-induced vomiting or over-exercising after binge eating.

Food is 'like a drug'.

People with a binge eating disorder are compared to drug and alcohol addicts more often than other eating or food disorders. Some binge eaters describe a binge by saying they 'numb out' or 'go into the zone' during one. You can stop drinking alcohol or taking drugs by going cold turkey, but you need food to survive. You can't go cold turkey and stay off food forever. To win the battle, you need to develop your own unique skill set of secret inner-weapons to be content in a world where food is everywhere, all the time. It's about developing a relationship with food that serves you and your health.

What is Binge Eating?

A 'binge' occurs when you eat – even when you're not hungry – a large amount of food in a short amount of time and you feel compelled to eat and finish what you've started. It also involves severe distress and an impulse where emotion – not hunger – drives the need to binge.

More often than not, you hide the evidence that you've eaten it.

You feel a lack of control over what or how much you eat.

It's important to note that binge eating is not simply overeating on Christmas Day or overindulging in your favourite food every now and then. There is a distinct more challenging layer here. Binge eating occurs repeatedly and is often about suppressing or avoiding deep layers of unresolved emotion.

Often short extreme fasts or periods of severe restrictive patterns and extreme diets are a response to the guilt and shame of a binge period.

The Facts.

Millions of people worldwide are affected by eating disorders. Due to the secrecy of the illness, research and studies are often under-estimated. Eating disorders are complex in their nature and are becoming more common. Many people do not seek treatment.

There is a consensus that eating disorders, disordered eating and body image issues have increased worldwide over the last 30 years – and continues to rise.

A binge eating disorder (B.E.D.) is the most common of all eating disorders. It is not picky either – all races at any age can succumb to it and it affects both men and women equally.

Secret Wrappers.

Because of the type of relationship they have to food, and the remorse, shame and guilt after the binge, people who binge eat often become secretive about their eating habits and have secretive behaviours around food. They may eat 'normally' with others, and then secretly binge on food and hide evidence of the episode. The person who binge eats has a 'face' that looks normal, but bingeing often gets to a point where it interferes with lives, relationships, work and play. Quite frequently clients who come to see us have been bingeing for years before they had the courage to tell anyone.

We believe food deprivation (dieting) does not work, it simply exacerbates the troubled relationship to food by repeating the deprivation versus binge cycle.

We've written this book because we get you. We wanted to write the kind of book we would have loved (and needed) in years gone by. We are both adamant that the book does not advocate diets.

We believe food deprivation (dieting) does not work, it simply exacerbates the troubled relationship to food by repeating the deprivation versus binge cycle. But the main reason we never advocate dieting is because those who design the diets ignore emotional hungers.

Diets can help to radically transform your body, but they ignore the emotional relationship to the food and eating, the emotional relationship to potential past trauma and hurts.

We start a diet, we use willpower to stick to it, we follow it religiously, we restrict our food, we reject our food and we go hungry and get upset. Sometimes it 'works', but a lot of people end up gaining weight back.

It goes without saying, those who come up with fad diets do not consider the importance of the emotional relationship to our body and the all-important relationship to ourselves. But more about those relationships and the do's and don'ts of dieting later.

Typical behaviours and emotional states of a binge eater include:

- You eat large amounts of food quickly
- You hide your eating habits, perhaps by eating in secret or hiding wrappers in the bin so that others can't see what you have eaten
- You drive to multiple fast food restaurants just so no one knows how much you are eating
- You eat continuously throughout the day, with no planned mealtimes
- You feel stress or tension and use food to make yourself feel good
- You are embarrassed over how much you are eating
- You suffer from embarrassment, shame and guilt post binge and concerning eating habits
- You often feel numb while bingeing, like you are 'not there'. It's as if you eat on autopilot.

Signs you could be using your emotions to binge eat could be:

- Eating large meals when not feeling physically hungry
- Eating when you are bored, upset, angry etc.
- Craving fatty foods, carbohydrates or sugary foods
- Eating after you are full
- Eating for the sake of eating, even things you don't like
- Eating until your belly hurts, being uncomfortably full
- Rarely feel a sense of fullness or satisfaction
- Eating when you are not aware of it
- Secretive behaviours around food

Some other signs may be:

- Preoccupation with eating, food, body shape and weight
- Increased sensitivity to comments relating to food, weight, body shape, exercise
- Extreme body dissatisfaction, low self-esteem and shame about appearance
- Feelings of extreme shame, distress, sadness, irritability, anxiety and guilt during and after a binge

Both of us understand the severity of binge behaviours and believe they should be more widely recognised and appropriate treatment should be available. Understanding what has made you vulnerable and brought on your binge eating can be very difficult. We truly want to ensure that no one ever feels alone in the struggle, and if you do then please reach out.

If this sounds familiar, you might be thinking, "What the f*** is wrong with me? Why can't I get some control over this?" We know that feeling pretty well.

*"What the f*** is wrong with me?*
Why can't I get some control over this?"

We've written this book because we both strongly believe that there is lack of information, guidance and practical strategies out there to help people who have – diagnosed or undiagnosed – bingeing behaviours. We also believe that many of these strategies will help people caught up with other eating issues.

Imagine a solution that gives you an easy and stress-free relationship with food so you can just enjoy your life.

There is no single cause of Binge Eating Disorder, but there are a combination of factors that contribute to the condition:

- A binge eater will have a history of frequent or restrictive dieting
- They are affected by social factors such as the value placed on the 'perfect' body or size, critical comments about their shape, weight or eating or body image
- A history of weight stigma
- Traumatic experiences or events or painful childhood memories
- They may also have difficulty expressing emotions and feelings in daily life.

As soon as we choose to skip meals or restrict our food intake, whether this is based on the desire to lose weight or suppressing our hunger due to other reasons, our body will outsmart us.

It's our body's job to keep us alive. Whenever you choose to restrict your food intake, your brain causes you to seek out food and eat more. You may find that you are constantly thinking about food and are trying to 'manage your hunger' and generally feel as if you are always hungry. Only when your body feels safe will this end.

Awareness and acknowledging you have a problem.

To overcome the habit of binge eating, you need to do an honest appraisal of the reasons behind why it's happening and what your triggers are. Food is not going to solve the problem; it will just start another vicious cycle.

It is important that you accept and acknowledge where you are at right now, rather than trying to force yourself towards change. Acceptance of where you are now is the only place from which you can decide to move forward.

Megan says that her body shame was her most painful experience, but she couldn't move on from it until she acknowledged it. "I was always thinking about how fat I was to the point that I just became obsessed. I would overeat and then under eat until it become so blurred, that I just ended up restricting my food. It took so much courage to admit I was obsessed with my weight and how I looked. I was terrified, but I had to start treating my body better and start respecting it if I was going to get better. That didn't mean I had to love it straight away, but I had to start accepting it because I wasn't getting another one. I treated food like it was an enemy and it wasn't solving any of the problems I had! It was scary and uncomfortable to surrender to it, but once I did it was transformative. I started by looking at the foods I was restricting and the reason why. A complete game-changer for me."

Poor body image is a main trigger for binge eating and overeating. Studies show that people who dislike their body, are more likely to control their eating habits to control their body shape and weight.

At what point will you decide that you should be eating to live, as opposed to living to eat and, acknowledge that this is something that needs to be addressed? Remember, we can't change what we don't acknowledge.

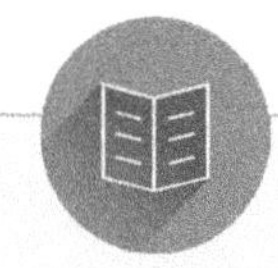

Megan's Story.

"I've had issues with food and poor body image for as long as I can remember," says Megan.

At around nine years old, a relative told Megan to stop eating because she was already fat. She meanly suggested Megan should eat only lettuce.

"I was suddenly paralysed and shell shocked." Megan remembered thinking, "Fat! Lettuce!! Was I that bad?"

For the next few days, Megan's youthful solution was to do exactly that. She rejected all food, except lettuce. "My mother discovered what I was doing. She yelled at my relative and told me to ignore what the relative had said."

Megan remembers her mother telling her she was gorgeous and normal and healthy. "But something had happened in my head," Megan says. "My relationship with my body changed that day. The battle in my head had started."

Megan remembers being called 'chubby', as if it was an endearment and supposed to make her feel special.

"I had become aware of my body, and I used to feel shocked each time I heard the judgments. But it wasn't until later that the war became action and I began the restriction and bingeing cycle."

In her early 20s, Megan wrestled with the battle of wanting to eat, but not wanting to put on weight. There wasn't a meal plan or diet that could save her. "Believe me, I tried everything along the way," she says.

"I starved myself for periods of time until I could no longer cope, then I would binge. The cycle continued; I was so ashamed. I never told anyone about what I did until I was ready to acknowledge the truth and to learn how to change it."

Throughout those years, on the outside Megan seemed fine, and everyone else thought so too. "But I clearly wasn't," says Megan.

Karyn's Story.

"I have a memory of my brother and I being given money to catch the bus to school. Instead of riding the bus, we used to walk and use the money to buy sweets and treats."

Karyn recalls she would have been six at that time. She learned at that very early age that with sweets came power. "I was a somebody – the other kids suddenly loved me."

Karyn learned that food buys you love and respect, and, more specifically, it was the sweets that especially had power. "So, whenever I've felt inadequate or triggered in the years since, my go-to binge was always chocolate or sweets."

"I was daddy's little girl, but my world fell apart when at the age of 10 I lost my daddy to cancer." Karyn's young age combined with her adoring love for her father meant that she hadn't realised her father was dying. As far as she remembers she wasn't told, nor did she notice that her father had been sick prior to his death. "I just remember lying in bed with him listening to classical music. I know now it was because he was sick and too weary to get out of bed, but I thought of it as our special time together. I can look back now and be grateful for those memories."

Karyn continues, "It has only just come to me while writing this book, that I probably don't like listening to classical music now because Daddy is not here to enjoy it with me. Funny how our brains work for us and against us, isn't it?"

Karyn's parents married young, both came from religious families where it was common to give each other holy cards and attend church every Sunday. "When Dad got sick with cancer, Sunday church services were reduced to holidays and, after Dad died, we never seemed to make it to a Sunday service again."

Karyn's mother had to find work after the death of her husband, she had to sell their café and then worked as the cook at a restaurant. Karyn would often visit her there after school. Then something changed, her mother started to let her hair down. "My mother became a party gal. She was smoking, drinking, and swearing, she was the life of every party. My mother came from a very big, close-knit family, she was one of sixteen brothers and sisters, so I had many cousins to hang out with growing up. Our family get togethers were always like big parties and my mother was the fun one to be around."

Karyn began to help her mother around the house, she cooked the meals and became very independent. "We had some great family parties at our house which always involved lots of food and alcohol. The parties would sometimes go on for days." Sometime later, her mother was introduced to Graeme, a fun loving and lovely man. It was a relief for Karyn to see her mother happy again. They became a happy, loving family.

Two years after Graeme married her mother, Karyn woke to a loud voice and what she thought was her mother's laughter. "But it wasn't laughter. I jumped out of bed to see what all the fuss was about. To my horror our lovely Graeme had been taken from us too. He had died in his sleep and it was my mother's heart-wrenching cry that I had mistaken as laughter."

Karyn and her family's world fell apart yet again "I was 15 years old this time, I had experienced more grief than anyone at that age should ever have to experience."

Karyn remembers the things that comforted her when she was growing up. "I used to go to the shops to get Mum chocolate to ease her pain. I remember that chocolate heals and soothes many things. I remember partying and that alcohol masks pain and hides your feelings. You could survive anything if there was chocolate in the house, a good party to enjoy and lots of alcohol to consume.

Bingeing, for Karyn, became her eating secret. "I learned all those years ago, that food, and especially of course those chocolates and sweets, helped me disconnect from myself and the world. Just like my mother, I would survive if I had my sweets, if I had a good dose of alcohol and a dash of superficial fun, I could be 'happy' and do anything."

She adds, "Of course, you can't eat that way for years and not expect some consequences. My health suffered, but more importantly, so did my value and self-esteem."

Karyn remembers the constant judgements from herself and others over the years, as the effects of bingeing took their toll on her health and weight. "Feeling imperfect is exhausting. I let it prevent me from feeling any joy and happiness for most of my life after my dad and Graeme died."

Karyn and Megan:

We share these stories not to enlist pity. We share these stories because we want you to know, we get you.

Your story might be different, or there might be glimpses of similarities, it doesn't matter about the stories. What matters is that we've been there. We understand there are many different reasons why we start these habits. There are also many different triggers. None of us are the same, and yet, we all are connected. We are connected by our humanness, our perfect imperfection. We just didn't realise we were already perfectly perfect, just as we are. We had to learn to love and accept ourselves, perhaps for the first time in our lives. Whatever did, or didn't happen, whatever we should have or could have done to change the outcome so far, nothing else matters except deciding we are still perfect, as we always were since the day of our birth.

The only important thing is, if we want to acknowledge where we are now, and we're ready to decide we want to do something differently, then we simply need to learn different habits, that's all.

That's what we are here to help you find.

- To be ready to address where you are
- To acknowledge and be okay with where you are today
- To decide and learn how to make a plan for what you want for tomorrow
- To discover the steps to put that plan into place
- To find the support from people who know who you are and accept every tiny cell and aspect of you

Let's begin by addressing in Chapter 2, what's on your plate. Is it emotions or food? Once you acknowledge where you're at right now, you'll be able to start using our strategies to make one small change at a time.

We've both been there. We get you. Let's do this together.

You can download free resources at
www.eatingsecrets.com.au/resources

CHAPTER 2
What's on Your Plate? Emotions or Food?

"Food can fill your stomach; It cannot fill your soul.

Food can nourish your body; It cannot physically nourish your heart and mind.

Food can make your taste buds experience pleasure or displeasure and your brain release feel good endorphins; It cannot make the real you happy.

Food can give you momentary pleasure; It will not give you lasting pleasure.

Food can distract you from your emotional pain; It cannot solve that pain."

—Adapted from the poem What Food Can Do, Author Unknown

The Art of Secret Eating.

We live in a society which is obsessed with food, a society that has learned to associate happy, sad, celebratory, social, non-social and every other kind of event or emotion with food and eating. For many of us secret eating starts habitually because, in time, we find it harder to distinguish physical hunger from habitual hunger, emotional hunger and triggers like mood.

There are so many mixed-up triggers when it comes to choosing when and what to eat.

How do you know you feel genuinely hungry?

- Do you recognise the difference between genuine hunger and that 'other' hunger?

- Do you put food in your mouth just because it's in front of you?

- Have you ever felt 'hungry' again soon after eating a meal?

- Do you find that you eat just because the clock tells you?

You'd think it would be easy to identify if you are hungry or not, but the experience of hunger feels different for everyone. There is no right or wrong way – just your way. It's equal parts biological instinct, and a learned response connected to an emotional or habitual trigger.

Megan says, "I was a habitual eater, so I would only eat at a set time through the day, whether I was hungry or not. I've always been someone who needs a routine and some structure to my day, and eating became something I did on schedule, without even realising it. I was so out of touch with whether I was hungry or not, I just ate when it was time. If I missed my time slot, then I missed my chance. And I got really good at having an excuse to miss my 'scheduled mealtime'. I had to re-learn to listen to my body, when it tells me it's hungry on its schedule rather than on mine. It worked out that my new schedule was eating within an hour of waking up and then every four hours after that. I still had a routine – just a healthier one for me.

When mood affects our food.

We would hazard a guess that 90% of the time when we 'feel' hungry, we haven't consulted our body to reveal the truth. We've learned to allow our mood and other external triggers to affect our choice and intake of food.

When we turn to food for comfort, it says a lot about our emotional needs. The food isn't the food problem.

When we turn to food for comfort, it says a lot about our emotional needs. The food isn't the food problem. What else is going on? Have a look at your mood – what's coming up? Because whatever is coming up is controlling your behaviour with food.

Have you ever experienced thinking about a delicious food and suddenly being ravenous, even though you weren't remotely hungry a moment ago?

There are many ways to be triggered, especially by our senses, such as *seeing* our favourite food or by just *smelling* it. Imagine walking past a bakery and smelling the waft of freshly baked bread or inhaling the smell of bacon as it sizzles in the pan.

Activity.

Do these or other similar triggers cause all kinds of delicious feelings and urges?

On a scale of 1 to 10, 10 being the most, how much does the trigger make you want to eat or drink that food? And at what level of that scale would you eat it or drink it? Even if your body genuinely wasn't hungry? Use this activity to bring awareness to the next time you're triggered.

Megan says her weakness is still a packet of Cheezels or cheese Twisties (Australia), (in the USA the equivalent would be Cheetos). "For me, there's something about the sound as I open the packet and hear the crunch while I eat."

If you find yourself craving crunchy foods like crisps or anything that you bite down on and has a crunch, it might mean you're dealing with feelings of anger and frustration. Is there anything going on that angers or frustrates you?

Megan has found how to deal with that trigger. "Here's the thing, I know this salivary response is my brain triggering a habitual hunger and an emotional urge for the sensory experience. The difference is I know now I get to choose my response to the trigger. "

Difference between head hunger and real hunger.

It's important to make the point that sometimes we all turn to food for enjoyment or comfort, even when our body is not physically in need of nutrients. This is normal.

However, the difference is that many of us are out of touch with what genuine hunger feels like in the body, and what the sensation of comfortably satisfied feels like. Many of us have no idea we've eaten more than enough until the feeling of over-fullness kicks in.

Reactivating and knowing your body's signal for genuine hunger is an extremely important early step.
Head Hunger is another way of saying 'habitual or emotional hunger.' Unless you know the signals to tell them apart from a genuine hunger or thirst, unhelpful food patterns continue unchecked.

Here is a quick run-down of the difference

Head Hunger (Habitual and Emotional):

- The urge happens from your neck up
- The pang often starts as a thought, then escalates quickly
- It is often sudden and urgent
- It will be for a specific food or food group
- Alternatively, it doesn't matter what food it is, as long as there's lots of it and it's available now or can be made available with a quick drive to buy it
- Does not abate, even when you are full or after a small amount
- You experience a short emotional satisfaction and then often feel numb, or regret, shame or guilt
- Involves automatic or 'autopilot' eating (not noticing how much you eat until the trigger to stop occurs, e.g. a trigger to stop could be the packet is empty)
- You have random food cravings or time-specific urges, e.g. 11am munchies at work with a hot beverage
- You know you are full, but when out socialising you still have what others are having
- You still think of food or eating after you are full, e.g. with either more cravings or with frustration or remorse

- You find yourself wanting to eat so you can feel better about a situation

Real Hunger (physical):

- The urge happens from the stomach
- The urge grows much more slowly
- The urge is for a variety of nutrient rich food
- It is a patient and calm feeling
- Goes away once you've eaten enough
- Your physical, mental and emotional bodies feel sated
- Involves deliberate choices and conscious awareness of your body's needs
- The body is consulted, and decisions about which foods to eat will often be made based on what is best for the body, health and vitality
- Real hunger doesn't trigger you or make you feel bad about yourself

Emotional eating isn't about 'your eyes being bigger than your belly.'

Emotional or habitual eating is about using food to fulfil automated urges, uncomfortable emotions or sensations. When we eat in response to head hunger, we are fueling our body with food that it does not need.

Speaking from experience, when we were stressed or depressed or anxious, it felt good to have something to chew on, so our focus was about the act of chewing, the sounds, smells and sensations. Our attention was diverted from the 'feelings' going on beneath the sensory experience.

"For me," says Megan, "I learned to chew and swallow more to avoid how I was really feeling. I didn't know how to express myself in a healthy manner."

The food you hoover to avoid dealing with feelings always come with strings attached – weight gain and shame.

When a craving doesn't originate from 'nutritional hunger', eating won't ever satisfy it.

Once you become aware of this, you are blessed with an opportunity to figure out, or seek help to discover, what is really going on for you. You can start paying attention to other areas of your life, and the situations or tricky questions you've avoided.

Remember in Chapter 1 when we mentioned that your body's job is to keep you alive? Your body knows what it needs. But you need to become the expert again to listen to it and meet its needs in order to find your original internal signal of genuine hunger and fullness

Activity.

Trigger Foods

Make a list of your trigger foods – the ones you know or suspect you can't resist and are 'bad' for you. Take a few minutes to journal whatever comes to mind about each one.

- Make a note about what the food smells like, how it tastes, what it looks like, the textures.
- Write about its history in your life, perhaps the first time you had that food.
- Were you with others or by yourself?
- Is there an emotion that the food makes you feel or symbolises to you?

1.	
2.	
3.	
4.	
5.	
6.	
7.	
8.	

Download your 'Trigger Food' chart by visiting www.eatingsecrets.com.au/resources

Nourish or Punish – Are you eating enough food?

Our brain has a built-in survival mechanism. If you are restricting food, (such as a low-calorie diet), your brain will trigger a warning that starvation is imminent. It triggers you and your body to do whatever is necessary to keep you alive. The brain and body have no idea that it's Monday and you've started your 'diet.'

Your brain's primitive response is to trigger stronger urges so that you eat more and 'stock-up' reserves to tide you over until the imminent danger has passed. Restricting food is the #1 reason for binge eating.

When you 'restrict' your food intake and feel internal stress about that, your brain and body are craving for the things you are withholding. According to your brain, your body needs it. Likewise, when you deny yourself the 'bad' food, the internal stress will mean your brain will trigger you to remember you want it or need it even more.

What you resist persists. The more you restrict and suppress urges without dealing with them to remove them appropriately, the more power food has over you. To the point sometimes, we've heard clients say, "But the food calls me from the fridge, it speaks to me from the pantry."

The more you restrict and suppress urges without dealing with them to remove them appropriately, the more power food has over you.

This can be the biggest and most challenging trigger of binge eating. Breaking this cycle is hard. We have been conditioned to diet and then restrict and then binge. The more we restrict the foods we love, the more appealing they start to become.

Have a think about your thoughts around food. Do you believe that you shouldn't be eating certain foods, and do you restrict them and then binge on them? Start integrating those foods one at a time – even if that seems scary.

Once you have identified the emotions that triggered the urge to eat, you can seek out other ways to comfort and calm yourself without turning to food. You might stress, feel overwhelmed or frustrated because you just 'wish' you had an escape from the constant chatter in your head. You won't obtain inner peace and acceptance with binge foods. A truly hungry person will eat a range of nutritious foods, wherever they are, whoever they're with. They don't hide away to eat or eat only in private.

As an emotional or habitual eater, even a binge eater, when you eat, you seek the pleasure of food and avoid the pain of hunger.

From a biological standpoint, we are all programmed to seek pleasure and avoid pain. It is the most primitive response of the human nervous system.

However, the mind-hack is – you can't receive the pleasure unless you are aware that you are engaging in it. So, if you are not paying attention to what you are eating, you miss the pleasure. Pleasure brings satisfaction, satiety and relaxation.

If a secret pleasure is something sugary, or fast food and takeout, initially you receive a massive dose of pleasure by eating that food. If you don't have it, your brain associates that lack as pain (stress).

Your behaviour – to binge – has been formed by pain and pleasure from the day you were born: your upbringing, societal influences, the media and the human need for acceptance, love and attention.

The Food Industry spends billions of dollars engineering food-like substances to target these innate needs. They use high concentrations of sugar, starch, salt, fat and oil. They then spend trillions more on branding and marketing to convince us that our innate human needs will be met by buying and eating that food or drinking that beverage. The messages tell us that our happiness, safety, connection, our need for love and acceptance will be sated when we do.

Your brain (not the real you), avoids the uncomfortable feelings (lack of connection, lack of acceptance, love and safety), by seeking pleasure in the food.

Binge eaters seek pleasure from food and the act of eating itself.

What would your body say if it could talk?

Activity.

Try this technique and with practice you will detect signals that notify you when it's time to start and stop eating.

The next time you eat, pause.
- What part of you feels hungry? Is the urge above the neck or below?
- Place your hand over the area that is 'talking' to you.
- If your hand moves to your stomach ask, "Is my body genuinely hungry?"
- Scan for hunger sensations; growling; an empty, hollow or queasy sensation.
- If so, rate your level of hunger between 1 – 10 (1 being starving, 5 is satisfied and 10 is over full)
- If hunger ranks between 1 and 4 then it is time to eat.
- If the rating is higher than 5, then the urge is not physical, it's emotional or habitual. Ask yourself, "What am I trying to fulfil instead?"

For example, begin eating at 4 on the scale and stop eating at 7, this way you will avoid ever feeling starving or stuffed. You can also learn to detect the difference between real hunger and emotional hunger.

If your hand lands on your head, heart, or somewhere else, then the urge to eat is triggered by an emotional or habitual need. Be curious about what is happening for you **in that moment**.

- Would any food be welcome or only tempting food?
- What food is your head or heart asking for?
- Be specific – a food group, a specific food or a taste like spicy, salty.
- Have a glass of water, then check in and repeat the exercise in a few minutes

Janine's story.

Janine's 'go to' binge food was always hot chips and gravy. In a clinic session she remembered being allowed to walk by herself to the takeaway shop.

Janine said, "This shop was the first place I'd spent my tooth fairy money. At home we always ate healthy food and the chips were a treat."

After delving deeper, Janine revealed that she liked this walk to the shop; she was on her own, she felt independent and could make her own choice.

"It's like I had my first taste of freedom, I remember being happy as I walked, I felt very calm."

She admitted, "Every time I binge, I have that feeling too."

Once Janine had made the connection, the urge for hot chips and gravy had no further power over her and she released the food craving. She was able to make a connection to other things in life that made her feel happy and calm that didn't involve food.

Melinda's story.

Melinda's binge eating pattern was triggered by emotions. She was the fifth child of a single parent family. She remembered that money was always tight. "I remember Mum not eating meals so us kids would have enough. It made me sad."

She continued, "My grandmother would pick me up from school and make me eat something every day, then she would give me milk and cookies."

Melinda loved feeling happy when she had that one-on-one attention from her grandmother. "It was very special," she said.

Melinda observed the pattern of bingeing as she got older and realised she had equated happiness with eating and sadness with starving.

Megan's Story:

I was restricting my food to the point of starvation. I would spend most of the day obsessing over food and feeling hungry, but still I couldn't lose weight. I had become obsessed with exercising and ate less and less. I joined gyms and hired personal trainers because I'd been told that weight loss is not that hard if you simply burn more calories than you take in. Those words tortured me for years and set up an unhealthy mindset that clouded my judgment on what 'healthy' really means. It also started a terrible 'restrict and reward' cycle. I got to a point in my own mind where I would only eat after I had exercised for a certain amount of time to then justify the food I would consume. However, after restricting myself for so long I would binge. On food or wine. Generally, both.

I couldn't sustain the food restrictions and would cycle between starvation and bingeing over many years. I used to only feel 'good' when I ate healthy and 'bad' when I ate something I shouldn't have. But when I tried to 'do the right thing' with food I was left frustrated, confused and utterly depleted. My sense of self became entirely linked with food and how much I would eat. I was constantly faced with new circumstances and situations where I just didn't know what to do.

What was going on with me? It wasn't what I was eating – but something was eating away at me.

Nothing changed for me until I made the decision to re-educate myself about a healthy relationship to food and my body. I had to look at my thoughts and beliefs around food. It was changing the littlest habits that made all the difference. I had to learn how to express what I needed to say, instead of using food or alcohol to stuff down my emotions. And I had to trade self-criticism for self-love and self-care.

We'll provide further case studies in the following chapters, including more about both our stories too.

In the next chapter we address simple techniques to cope with the emotional and habitual 'stuff' that triggers us to binge, without resorting to stuffing our face with food.

CHAPTER 3
Face Your Stuff – Don't Stuff Your Face

"If you try to lose weight by shaming, depriving, and fearing yourself, you will end up shamed, deprived and afraid. Kindness comes first, always." Geneen Roth

The Secret 'Stuff.'

Imagine trying to clean your house and instead of using the vacuum cleaner you use a broom.

You sweep the dirt under the rug. Time goes by, you know the secret dirt is there but it's unseen, no one will be any the wiser. Every cleaning day, you do the same again and sweep that 'secret stuff' under the rug in another corner so it doesn't build up in one place in case people notice.

Our 'secret stuff' is the emotions, hurts and fears we tend to keep hidden: our shame, self-doubt, fears, longings, truths, desires, bad habits, dreams and disappointments. When did you start? Perhaps you began sweeping stuff under the carpet when you were young, perhaps to feel accepted, approved and loved.

When we experience uncomfortable or intense emotions, we do our best to avoid them. As humans, we are pre-programmed to go to extreme lengths to avoid pain and suffering and seek pleasure.

Even if that means we are adding more pain and suffering to our existing pain and suffering.

We hope the pain will go away, perhaps we kid ourselves that we'll go back and deal with it later, just not now. If something happens and we don't have the skills to deal with it, we just sweep it under the rug and hope it doesn't trip us up.

Let's call this your comfort zone, because it's where you have learnt to be comfortable. At the time you think it's easier to stay there, but there comes a time when the space under the rug is so full you start to trip up.

Maybe you dismiss the 'stuff' by harshly thinking, "I just need to get over it"

The longer we avoid our 'secret stuff' and let the 'dirt' build under the rug, the bigger the pain becomes. Our brain is programmed to avoid it and seek more pleasure.

At some stage you need to face your stuff. You need to look under that rug and properly remove what's there. We live in fear that someone will discover our secret dumping ground, and we pray that the rug doesn't get pulled out from underneath us.

When you face your stuff and stop dismissing your emotional pain, it's important to know you'll feel uncomfortable at first. But do this without any self-criticism, judgements or blame. Once you work through the initial discomfort, you will become open and curious so that you can get comfortable with your stuff. This means acceptance, and a sensation of inner peace.

It doesn't make what happened right or wrong, it's simply time to process the emotion and let it move through you, so that you can clear your stuff and move on.

It's about noticing what's no longer working for you and getting you out of your self-imposed prison. It's in moving through the discomfort that you will find the value and wisdom of an experience.

It will take practice, but then when 'stuff' comes up, you can put it in the bin where it belongs.

Secret Emotions.

Psychoanalyst Wilhelm Reich observed the effects of repressed emotions on the body, he called it 'body armour.' As a person accumulates unprocessed emotions throughout childhood, they adapt to the environment and their body (and character) learns to shield them from additional emotional pain with that body armour.

We live in a world where we are taught to avoid certain emotions and act 'strong'. The messages we're given include 'don't cry' and 'don't be sad' and to 'look on the bright side' because 'things could be a lot worse'.

Instead of processing emotions, most of us learn to avoid or control them and will 'distract' ourselves. This applies to good and bad emotions.

Emotions are like colours of the rainbow and serve a purpose, such as signaling things we should be paying attention to.

The long-term consequence of repressing emotions results in the vicious cycle of habits that have been learned over time to avoid the 'stuff'.

People who struggle with binge eating are often disconnected from their emotions and they subconsciously continue to binge as a temporary way to cover up their feelings. To overcome bingeing, you need to deal with the underlying repressed emotion, bring it to your awareness and learn how to deal with your emotions in a healthier way.

It's very important that you choose to face what you may have swept under the carpet in a safe way. The 'secret stuff' doesn't have to define you, but it has trapped you. When you address the underlying reasons why you stuff your face with your 'go to' binge food or beverage, you remove the years of dirt trapped beneath the surface and take off the years of applied band-aids. Only then can the wound heal.

Secret Truths.

Maybe your Truth is not the Truth? We spend most of our time 'living up to' other people's truths and half-truths and expectations – the illusions and delusions, the misconceptions and labels. 'Your Truth' and 'the truth given to you' are two entirely different things.

For many of us, we have emotional attachments to food – whether we know it or not. Do you associate food with love? Or relaxation? Do you eat when you are bored, stressed or lonely? These are all 'truths'. They are not bad or wrong, they are emotional responses.

E-Motion.

When you experience your emotions, you allow them to move through you. You free up the space in your body where the energy was blocked. When you use food or other substances to hide from feeling the emotion (or keep hold of it in the case of some good emotions), you become stagnant. You repeat the same cycle over again. Yet wonder why you're not getting better, why you can't change a habit or improve your life.

The word emotion itself has the solution within it.

E-MOTION

E = ENERGY + MOTION = MOVEMENT

Energy affects us in ways you can't consciously be aware of. Everything is made of energy and has its own unique vibration, including you. Everything is in a constant state of receiving and radiating energy.

Your emotions are meant to be experienced, so they move through you and out of your body. When you practice that, you experience growth, you change as the wisdom within the emotion becomes available to you.

Then the emotion is gone.

Secret Sounds.

Certain sound frequencies have calming effects on the physical body and help clear the energy of your space.

Sound is an energy itself; it can create a deep energy shift which will allow you to release the emotional stress. Using sound is a simple way to move energy by raising vibration, creating space and breaking up our stagnant energy, as sounds can wake up the mind and our energy. When you feel lethargic, make a little noise to wake up your energetic body.

Activity.

This technique is to make sounds to help you release the emotions. Find a safe space where you'll be alone. Sometimes going out in nature is helpful.

It's important that you feel the emotions and ensure your safety in expressing sounds. Recognise when you feel the emotion and be willing to embrace it.

Take 10 minutes to go through the list below and make your version of the sound you think matches the list. It may seem weird, even a little uncomfortable or silly, but we promise it will start to feel easier and it will create a healing as it is released. If it triggers you to feel fear, then start with that as the first emotion to deal with.

If you are feeling this: fear, anger, frustration, impatience, distress, irritation, bitterness, boredom, judgment, helplessness, resentment – Make this sound: scream/shout

If you are feeling this: shock, over-excitement, in need of nourishing, exhaustion, tired, jealous, craving attention, not good enough, despair, gladness, happiness, excitement – Make this sound: laughter

If you are feeling this: annoyed, nervous, sadness, hurt, guilt, depression, unfulfilled, regret, panic, worry, contempt, masking the emotions – Make this sound: deep sigh or cry

If you are feeling this: anxiety, panic, scared, restless, impatience, terror, frustration, addiction, worn out, inadequacy, dread, paranoia – Make this sound: moan/groan

If you are feeling this: rejection, criticised, disapproval, doubt, disgust, deprived, envious, unappreciated, neglected, hunger, feel empty, disappointment – Make this sound: sing

Hannah's Story.

Hannah remembers her mother having mental health issues when she was a child. Her mother would storm into her room when she was asleep as a little girl. Her mother would scream at her and throw Hannah's things around the room. "She would pull things out of the wardrobe and drawers, raging at me," Hannah told us.

She continued, "I was terrified of Mother, I wouldn't cry or say anything. I learned quickly that if I cried or said anything when my mother was in that state, there would be consequences."

Hannah learned to stop expressing her feelings in fear of the consequences. Even to the point that for many years she was not being able to 'feel' at all and instead, when faced with intense feelings, she would binge eat.
We asked Hannah to keep a food journal. She began to notice a pattern. When she had a bad day at work, she noticed that evening she would 'numb' her stress by bingeing.
"It was so helpful," she said. "Once I made the connection, I realised that I was eating my anger. I still feel anger, but I no longer eat it."

Karyn's Story.

My inner prison kept me safe because I had a belief that if I exercised, I would die.

I don't mean I was worried I would have a heart attack – well sometimes when I was breathless that thought did cross my mind, but it was an unconscious irrational fear.

My father died when I was 10. I remember when he fell off a ladder. His fall made big holes in the wall of the house. As a 10-year-old, I didn't consciously associate that incident with my father getting sick and then dying several months later.

Being 'daddy's little girl' I had a huge feeling of a hole in the wall of my heart; I could never talk to my daddy again.

I had previously been a very active sporty child, but when Dad died, I stopped doing active, sporty things which at the time for a kid who was sad and mourning the loss of her father, seemed normal. My way of filling those 'holes' was to binge.

It made me wonder, "What other false beliefs, and associations had my brain decided on to keep me safe? What else was my brain using food for to be my false 'savior'?

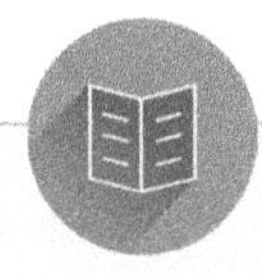

Megan's Story.

"You'd be a knockout if you lost weight"

Wow, right? I fell for it. When a guy would say that to me (or anyone else for that matter), it simply confirmed to me that if I lost weight, I'd get what I wanted.

I had the belief that I was fat and ugly, and clearly unkissable.

Were those words meant to cause me harm? Probably not. Just a careless comment. No one is completely immune to the words of other people. But the effect on me was profound and my internal war continued to rage.

I clung to the rejection. Although I had a very supportive family, I hid my feelings well. Probably too well. So well in fact, that my family and friends will be shocked when they read this book.

I hated looking in mirrors. I obsessively counted calories. I worked out at the gym to the point of exhaustion, but still felt shame. Every step I took I counted in my head. I would think about what I ate, what I didn't eat, how much I weighed, and how much I was going to lose after the 'next diet'. I would fall asleep wondering if I would lose weight the next day or gain it. As I lost weight people would tell me how good I looked, and to me it felt as though I was deemed 'more acceptable'. I was told I looked good 'now that I started looking after myself better' and had 'lost all that baby fat'. I felt devastated and lost more confidence. I was at my lowest point the more weight I lost. Looking back now, losing weight and looking good by other people's standards increased my value. My worth was measured by other people's comments about how I looked.

I was empty and sad and *knew* something was very wrong with me. I felt as though no one could see me. I felt ashamed and unlovable in every way, shape and form. I was in serious trouble, but no one mentioned it me, so I kept going. They noticed I'd lost weight but now I was 'hot', everything was cool, right?

I didn't realise that the amount of stress I was putting myself under was causing a lot of damage emotionally, mentally and physically.

In the next chapter we'll talk more about ways to deal with stress and how and why it triggers us to eat.

I'M SO OVERWHELMED, IT'S ALWAYS LEFT UP TO ME.

CHAPTER 4
Do you season your food with stress?

S.T.R.E.S.S.

S-Someone

T-Trying To

R-Repair

E-Every

S-Situation

S-Solo

The Secret about Stress.

Stress is a very big topic, but the big picture of stress is not the purpose of this book. Our purpose is to give you the basics so that you can understand the link between stress and bingeing. There are many great resources available if you'd like to read more generally about stress itself.

To simplify stress, we will refer to 'stress' as the stuff that triggers you to respond to a situation in an unhelpful way. To overcome the habit of bingeing it's important to understand that bingeing is simply your learned reaction to your individual good and bad stressors.

The only thing you can control is HOW YOU REACT AND RESPOND TO STRESS. You can't eliminate stress, but you can learn a more helpful response to it.

Bingeing and self-sabotage are both learned responses. Some of us learned to respond to stress in a helpful way and others of us not so much.

What is Stress Eating?

Stress eating is a coping mechanism. It's an emotional response to a stressor. If you stress eat, you'll either eat as a distraction to avoid a stressful situation (numb it) or seek a way to stimulate a different feeling (feel something else). It's a form of self-medication with food. If we are feeling stressed, food can distract us from our thoughts and feelings.

A binge eater can probably relate to the following:

- You think about the food you're not going to eat because the harder you try *not* to think about it, the more you think about it
- You try to ignore these thoughts and believe that you can rely on your willpower, but secretly know you can't
- BOOM! The stress trigger happens

The battle in your head amps up…

And then you eat…

And you feel like shit…

And then it happens again …

So how do you break that pattern?

To understand your stress eating patterns you need to know that it's an automatic behaviour which you do without thinking or without any real effort at all. Your coping mechanism then becomes a habit.

The first step to successfully beating that cycle, is to find your reason why you want to beat it. The strength of your 'why' will give you the power to focus on that, while your brain is learning how to change the response to the triggers. If your 'why' motivates you enough, the next step is to use that 'why' to keep you focused on resolving the emotional connection between the triggers and food.

If that connection is not resolved, you'll continue doing what you are doing.

Why do you do it?

Everyone has a 'why'. It's what motivates us and drives our behaviour. By knowing our 'why' we can understand our behaviour.

The Japanese have the term 'ikigai,' which can be translated to mean 'a reason for being.' This is anything that gives a deep sense of purpose to a person's life and makes it worthwhile. It is what you get up for every morning.

You've got to dig deep beneath the surface here and stop judging yourself. Instead, be curious, observe and make note of what you are searching for when you are triggered to eat. What's the emotional need?

Your 'why' can either guide you towards failure or success. If your 'why' for bingeing is stronger than your 'why' to stop, then you will be guided to failure based on your 'why'.

To overcome bingeing, you need to make sure your 'why' for success is more compelling, so you can stay on track when you're being tested by the binge monster and succeed in escaping the prison.

Activity.
Your Why.

Write your reasons for wanting to binge. Consider your 'why'.

- Are you sad and need comfort?
- Do you feel lonely and want company, someone to talk to?
- Are you angry and need to let off steam?
- Are you scared or anxious and need to feel safe?
- Perhaps the pattern is more about positive emotions, are you happy and want to celebrate?

Be curious and write what you know so far:

____

____

____

Now, consider your 'why' for wanting to break the binge cycle. Consider your 'why' and make it stronger and more compelling than your reasons to binge.

- Do you want to set an example for your kids?
- Do you want to feel healthy?
- The money you'll save by not buying binge foods can be spent on a holiday
- Do you want to wake up in the morning feeling contentment instead of shame?
- Wanting to enjoy food without the constant head talk
- Wanting to get through 12 hours without food being on your mind
- Wanting to enjoy life feeling fulfilled and happy

Be curious and write what you know you WANT – this is your 'WHY' for success:

____

On a scale of 1-10, with 10 being the most, how important is it to you to conquer the bingeing habit and to not self-sabotage your health again.

By identifying your 'why' and discovering your patterns you take some of the power back and have the chance to render the trigger powerless. Avoiding stress is impossible, so breaking those patterns is a way to escape the prison of bingeing.

Your thoughts create your beliefs, that trigger your feelings, that trigger your actions, that create your current reality.

How to cope with stress.

Stress Management needs to be a conscious choice to do something different about the stressors in your life.

- You need to change the way you think about the stress
- Monitor the beliefs that keep you stuck
- Ask yourself if you have developed a 'set of rules' about how to behave
- There is often a gap between the way things appear to be and what is real. Many times, when stress hits, your biggest enemy is how you look at that stress. You can think yourself into a much worse state of mind about whatever is or isn't going on, and then the bingeing monster strikes.
- Reframe your perspective to find the positive message in what's happening, to diffuse the stress and disrupt the pattern.

Relinquish Control.

What difficult feelings drive your desire to control your food or weight?

What is behind your need to control your food or weight?
- Do you long for love, acceptance or validation?
- Is thinness a status symbol for you?
- Do YOU judge others on their size and how they look?
- Do you believe you will be 'happy' if you're thin enough?

What secret fears, shame, or other feelings are behind it? What is motivating your need to control your food and weight?

When you accept you can't control every situation or the outcomes all of the time, you can learn to take the pressure off yourself. That pressure has only added to your stress in the past. We have enough external pressure in life, why add fuel to that? Perhaps it's time to be kind to yourself. Emotional Freedom Technique (EFT) or tapping is a great technique to help with stress and relinquishing control. We give a great demonstration of how EFT works in our online course.

Learn to Let Go and Just Breathe.

Food isn't going anywhere, there won't be a world shortage of the food you love tomorrow, so maybe you can let go of the need to have it right now. By paying more attention to your breathing, you can calm the fight or flight reaction that triggers the habit by breathing more consciously. Are you taking long deep breaths or are your breaths shallow? Is your breathing slow or fast? Be curious and adjust your breath until you feel calm.

Activity.

Breathing shush.

Adjust your posture. Are you breathing into the chest or lower down?

- With your head straight, roll your eyes up to the ceiling
- Put the palm of one hand on your forehead
- Take a long, slow deep breath, breathe in through your nose and let your belly fill with air and hold your breath to the count of three
- Put your pointer/index finger to your lips, as if you are shushing yourself
- Imagine this finger is a candle and it has a flame. Exhale your breath and imagine blowing the candle out to the count of 10
- Take at least three full, deep breaths and exhale completely, to really, really blow the candle out
- Take a moment to reflect on how you are feeling

The Secret F Word.

Include this new 'f' word into your life – feelings. Start connecting more with yourself and what is really going on and feel your full feelings. If you want, try and label them, notice what they feel like and where you can you feel them in your body. Feel the feelings underneath the desire to control your food and body.

When we are in an emotional state, we often don't know the differences between feelings, moods and emotions. We generally assume that they are the same, but the difference between them all is time. Sometimes you might binge when you 'feel in a mood' or might be going through a range of emotions or you just 'feel blah'. Once you understand the difference, you can then embark on a journey to understanding them.

Try this technique to uncover the differences.

Be present with what is happening right now with your thoughts, sensations, emotions and the environment. If something comes up, use curiosity rather than judgment. Simply observe and allow the thoughts to drift by just like clouds, without having to do anything in response. When you stay with your feelings for a little while you will begin to notice that you create space for them and they lose their power. It also allows you to feel calm and to make more rational decisions.

Miriam's Story.

Miriam became aware that in times of high stress she found herself mindlessly eating. Bingeing had become her way of calming down.

She said, "When I'm anxious or worried I eat a lot and feel out of control. I'm so embarrassed."

Once we practiced the simple breathing shush and reframed the things she was worried about, it helped her find perspective. From then on, in moments of stress, she was able to reduce bingeing dramatically and manage the quality as well as the quantity far more easily.

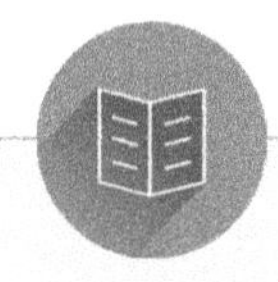

Karyn's Story.

Even before I formally trained as a practitioner, I was the person that friends came to for advice. I loved being able to help them, it made me feel special and loved. But I didn't understand why I would feel so crappy afterwards.

What I didn't realise was that I was holding their energy long after I had seen them. I felt their stress and it became another trigger to binge.

I have since found out that I am an empath, which means I take on other people's energy. A game changer for me was when I learned energy protection and clearing techniques.

A regular routine of crystal and energy protection, recalling my energy back to me and zipping up that energy morning and night allowed me to understand what my feelings are and which feelings belong to someone else. Doing this daily ever since has had an amazing positive impact for me.

Do you take on other people's stress? What is yours and what is not?

In the next chapter we address the way you communicate with food and how this can change everything.

Remember to download your free resources at
www.eatingsecrets.com.au/resources

THE CHOCOLATE CALLS TO ME FROM THE FRIDGE...

CHAPTER 5
Conversations with Food

"Don't dig your grave with your own knife and fork."

Old English Proverb

The Secret Conversations.

So how do you feel about food? Do you live to eat or eat to live?

One of the differences between binge eating and an addiction to drugs or alcohol is that you can't 'quit' food, you need food to survive. You can live forever without cigarettes, alcohol and hard-core drugs, but food is with you for life. You need to learn how to cultivate confidence about food, trust in yourself and your relationship to it. A relationship based on fear will never help you win this battle.

Developing a healthy relationship with food also involves maintaining a healthy relationship with yourself and your world. Food cannot be a substitute for feelings. Remember our feelings are meant to be energy + motion. So, staying stuck in the cycle of a poor relationship with food is never going to make you feel better long term.

The rules of the game are:

- Eat from a place of intention and not from a reaction
- There are no good or bad foods, simply healthy and unhealthy quantities of everything
- So, eliminate your 'no' or 'bad' food list
- Restricting (dieting), leads to stress and obsession for the mind of someone with a bingeing history
- Avoiding triggers WILL NOT WORK, you need to learn how to handle them better
- Being triggered means there is unresolved 'stuff' still to be resolved. You can't keep sweeping it under the carpet if you want change

The Diet Culture.

Your food intake is not only what you eat. It is what you watch, what you listen to, what you research, what you read and who you hang around with.

Even conversations about food rules, diets, meal plans and weight loss affect us all adversely, even if you don't identify with having any eating secrets.

There is an abundance of misinformation and misunderstanding around food and weight which prevents most people from losing weight for good. Be mindful of ALL the things you put into your body including emotionally, physically and spiritually.

When you become trapped by the dieting culture, it reduces your self-worth to a number or a size that our culture says is acceptable.

We have bookshelves bursting with 'diet' books: Atkins, South Beach, keto, the cabbage diet, juicing diet, and books that offer us rewards like 'points' for eating 'good'.

Beliefs we've been subliminally led to believe:

- If you don't fit that 'size', 'image' or 'number', there must be something 'wrong' with you
- You must be 'bad' and need to be 'fixed' or 'cured'
- Losing weight is 'good'; gaining weight is 'bad'
- Fat equals bad
- Carbohydrates are bad

There are 'naughty', 'sinful' and 'bad' foods, there are 'cheat' days, there are 'guilt-free' snacks. We have 'cleanses', 'clean foods' and 'detoxes' to rid your body of 'toxins'. There are 'processed foods' which we should replace with 'superfoods' or 'miracle foods' and live on 'broth'.

We even live in a time where we can get a 'beach body' or a 'perfect body' so we can wear our 'skinny jeans' and drink our 'skinny cappuccinos' while we read about the 'war on obesity.' We have 'big girl undies' that make us 'slim' and a wardrobe full of 'fat clothes' and 'when I'm skinny again' clothes.

It's our belief that one of the most toxic words in the English language is 'diet'. The diet industry is simply using good marketing playing on an emotional message. I read recently that Diet Coke was changed to Coke Zero to cater to men, as they didn't want to drink a diet drink.

It's our belief that one of the most toxic words in the English language is 'diet.'

Many long-term dieters, including us, were always trying to be 'good'. All that did was set us up for hunger, restriction, self-loathing and failure. Dieting is a direct cause of binge eating.

Let's change the word 'diet' to 'health'.

Perhaps you attempt to diet even harder after a night of binge eating? A binge eater will likely binge eat on foods that they're always trying to avoid. Strict food rules that tell you when, what and how much you are allowed to eat, or the labels that are assigned to the food, such as 'bad' food, will sometimes even trigger a rebellious and self-destructive binge eating episode.

Strong and healthy bodies come in all shapes and sizes. Let's change the word 'diet' to 'health'.

Belinda's Story.

A client of ours had one of the lesser known eating secrets. She had developed the secret habit of chewing and then spitting out food before swallowing. Her intent was that she could enjoy the taste, while preventing ingestion of the calories.

Belinda said, "I could still eat large amounts of food just like bingeing eating, but then I would deny myself the food, by spitting it out."

Belinda used to hide the spit balls in the bin, just like a binge eater hides food wrapping and evidence. This made the secrecy a major part of her enjoyment and shame about the habit. *"It filled my life, and the shame and self-disgust constantly played in my head,"* she added.

When Karyn and Megan took Belinda through a process to uncover potential triggers for starting the bingeing and restrictive pattern, Belinda remembered she'd had a strong emotional reaction when she was young to a throw away comment from a relative. *"A relative told me that I had chunky legs, I remember feeling very self-conscious from then on. I had been diagnosed with an autoimmune disease too, and became embarrassed by my body, the whole compulsive disorder started way back then."*

After learning that she was still consuming calories by chewing the food, maybe not as much as she would if she swallowed it as well, Belinda began to acknowledge where she was and what needed to change. With that information and the knowledge that she was at risk for possible ulcers and dental issues, it was enough of a wakeup call. Belinda was ready for help to break the habit and manage the cravings as she established a new, healthier relationship with eating and food.

Weight and the scales.

If you have a set of scales at home which you weigh yourself on, go get them and take them down to the nearest train tracks and throw them under a train. Get rid of them. Karyn calls scales 'the torture machine'.

If you find yourself stepping on the 'torture machine' every day; or stepping on them lightly in the hope of being lighter; or you step on and off several times hoping for a different outcome; or if the whole idea of stepping on the scales makes you anxious or ruins your day – then it's time to get rid of them.
The numbers on a scale don't measure how good of a person you are, nor are those numbers a measure of your success or how strong and healthy you feel. Your value can never be measured by a bathroom scale.

We both totally agree that looking good is important. However, if you think you need to be a certain 'size or look or weight' to feel good and be happy, you're the one standing in front of a speeding train. Your weight is not a measure of how good you are as a person.

How many times have you stepped onto the torture machine, read the number and it wrecked your day? We used to religiously weigh ourselves, often several times a day, to determine how we were 'measuring up'. The number told us if we'd been 'good'.

Your weight is not a measure of how good you are as a person.

Do you obsess over those numbers too? By weighing yourself you are re-enforcing unhelpful beliefs about yourself. (If you've lost weight, you're good; if you've gained it, you're bad.)

Megan recalls a friend with a little boy who, when he was four, would excitably jump on the bathroom scales and say, *"Oh look mummy – look how strong I am today."* Why can't we aim for that?

Weigh what really matters.

- You are far more powerful than the binge eating habit.
- Don't focus on numbers, your size, labels, or comparing yourself to others. Measure your self-esteem by how you feel when you look at your reflection. Start by improving that.
- Measure your success by how happy you are about you, not the world or what others do or do not do.
- Measure your health by how you feel inside.

Learn how to manage cravings.

Cravings are simply habits your brain has learned. Your brain's role is to keep you alive and breathing. If one of your learned habits initially makes you feel better, it uses that habit as a tool for survival. Then when you feel worse after doing the habit, your brain uses the habit to make you feel better again, and so the cycle continues.

A very helpful way to take control of the bingeing habit, especially as bingeing is usually something done secretly and alone, is when a craving happens, go and do something else. Such as take a deep breath. What are you feeling?

Your brain initiates a craving or urge to sustain the habit, if you ignore those urges the brain increases the urge because it senses you are in danger, (resisting the urge, triggers internal stress).

Your habit voice will trick you, "Go on, eat that cake, start tomorrow...you know you can't stop, just finish this, and we'll start again tomorrow."

So even though you don't want to do the habit, you will struggle with the voice the habit has developed or the voice it has given food.

Meet cravings with real food. Don't resist or ignore your feelings of hunger. Meet your craving head on and feed yourself with real food. This will be a hard habit to get into, but you will get used to it. Eat more of the good stuff and start developing a good health habit.

Meet cravings with real food. Don't resist or ignore your feelings of hunger. Meet your craving head on and feed yourself with real food.

Eat Like A Kid.

Do you remember when you were a kid, having to sit down at the dinner table, the TV was turned off and no snacks were allowed until you had finished your meal?

Kids can teach us to eat better. This doesn't mean that we play with our food or make funny faces at the dinner table, it means we appreciate how kids naturally choose what to eat and how much. Kids generally eat when they are hungry not when it is 'time' to eat. They also stop eating when they are full. There are no labels of good or bad food, off-limits foods, or 'fattening' foods. They don't fast or skip meals, they don't analyse their choices and they don't isolate themselves. They love eating with family and friends. Food is food – it doesn't consume their thoughts, it's just something that they do during the day. Food is seen as a great thing that helps us grow big and strong.

We always suggest to our clients to eat like a kid – BEFORE you were told otherwise.

When you experience a craving.

Say, "This is just a habit – it's NOT me. I dismiss the habit voice and dismiss the urge NOW." Then remember how you used to savour food as a child. Eat like a kid, make it last, enjoy the textures and flavours. Remember when you would spend forever eating an Oreo, or cream biscuit? Perhaps you made up your own system. Did you separate the two sides and lick the filling first? Did you nibble the corners?

Activity.
Prepare your mind - Trigger Activity

Make a list of the events and triggers that stimulate a binge episode, then acknowledge how that makes you feel after bingeing (regret, guilt, sick in the stomach, lethargic, angry). Then prepare your mind with what you could do instead of bingeing next time the trigger happens. Prepare your mind.

TRIGGER	HOW THAT MAKES ME FEEL AFTER BINGEING	WHAT COULD I DO INSTEAD?

You can download your 'Trigger Episode' chart by visiting www.eatingsecrets.com.au/resources

Next time you're in one of these scenarios, acknowledge it and accept, "I have the urge to binge."

Follow this with: "After bingeing I always feel ____________ ____"

Remind yourself how it has felt when you have binged (perhaps it was remorse, regret, physically sick, bloated, guilty or defeated).

Repeat what you choose instead: "I will do this ________ instead."

You can enhance this by spending a few minutes each day, rehearsing the different choices in your mind. Imagine yourself acting differently when triggered and feel what it feels like when you see your improvements in your mind's eye. Watch the action unfold as if you were watching a video. Are you the Actor or Director? How do other people in your video react to what's going on? What do you say? Play the scene in different ways until you are confident with the results.

Activity.
Two Plates.

Next time you think you're going to binge try this — it's a technique that helped us with sugar cravings.

Put your hands out in front you, with your palms turned up and imagine a plate on each hand.

The plate on the left side is sugary food and the plate on the right side is healthier options.

Focus on the left side, imagine how your body will feel after you eat the sugary food. (Bloated, awful etc.) Enlarge the image, notice how heavy you feel.

Now shift your focus on the right side, notice how light you feel after you eat the healthier option.

Make your choice from this headspace.

Remember it took you a long time to get to this place, so be kind to yourself by practicing the techniques. This is not about being perfect, that's part of the reason you might be here in the first place. Do the best that you can with the skills that you have. Good enough is enough. Simply choose to learn more skills and get better at those, rather than better at bingeing.

In Chapter 6 we discuss the blame game. When you let go of that game, you have a much better chance of overcoming bingeing and self-sabotage.

CHAPTER 6
It's Not Your Fault – The Bingeing Blame Game

"And no one will listen to us until we listen to ourselves."
Marianne Williamson

It's Not Your Fault.

You were born beautiful and amazing and you still are. Your binge eating does not define you. It is also not a life sentence.

Nothing you consciously did or didn't do initially caused you to start the binge eating habit. Please hear this, it is not your fault that the habit started. You were not born with a binge eating problem, so many factors contributed to establish the habit.

You need to get to the root cause of the binge. The 'stuff' that is so hidden that you may need help digging it out. It's like pulling the weeds out of a beautiful garden. The garden is still beautiful, but when the weeds are removed it really shines.

The initial reason will be different for everyone. There were circumstances that made you feel vulnerable and you did the best that you could with the coping skills you had at that time.

You need to get to the root cause of the binge. The 'stuff' that is so hidden that you may need help digging it out. It's like pulling the weeds out of a beautiful garden. The garden is still beautiful, but when the weeds are removed it really shines. Unfortunately, weeding takes time and work and those weeds are like habits that have formed, so you will have to also create new habits while doing the weeding to replace the old habits.

The habit started as your brain's way of keeping you safe. It triggered you to use food as a form of comfort or protection. Accept that it is just a habit.

Bingeing is simply a signal that it's time to work through past stress.

You might think that events or experiences don't bother you, but, deep down, if your brain learned at some stage of your life that this caused you stress, then until your brain learns a new way to deal with that stress that does not involve food, and until that new way becomes the new habit, your brain will continue saving you by producing cravings.

The past is important to understand why you may have felt unable to resolve outstanding emotional stress. Bingeing is simply a signal that it's time to work through past stress.

Secret Beliefs and Values.

Beliefs are something you hold true based on what your brain learned as a result of your experiences and reactions to those experiences.

A value is a long-lasting belief that helps us determine what is important. Values become the standard by which we live our lives and make our choices. Beliefs and values are the foundation of your current reality.

If what you believe is not congruent with what you think you want, you will always sabotage your efforts to change a habit.

Have you ever met anyone who has stood by their beliefs or values, even if it was to their detriment?

Often, we look at someone in that place and think, "Wow if only they weren't so stubborn."

If you look at some of your choices with an open and curious mind, you will find that you too have made choices in life based on your values and beliefs. Some of those choices did not and perhaps still do not serve you.

The thing about beliefs and values is if they no longer serve you, you can change them.

To do that, you must first become aware of which ones are not working for you. Then make a conscious choice to find what's needed to change your mind.

As children, many of us were told that we had to eat everything on our plate because there were less fortunate people starving in the world. From that childhood belief you may hold true a value that it's wasteful to throw away food.

If that belief is still serving you, fantastic. If it's not and you continue to eat even after you feel full, just because it's on your plate, then you get to choose to no longer eat excess food.

What are the things that you think you 'should' want or you used to want that no longer feel good to you?

Karyn's story.

Through a technique I learned some time ago, I realised that my number one core value is to enjoy life. Think about what that can mean to my relationship with food and alcohol. If my core value is to enjoy life and my brain has learned that food and alcohol help me do that, then that value has led to enjoying them so much that it turns to bingeing.

The first step is to be aware of the fact that you have the power to choose your beliefs and values. Then to understand what they are and make a distinction between what's helpful and unhelpful.

In the case of my core value, I had to learn the distinction between enjoying life and overindulging in food or alcohol. When I overindulge, I no longer enjoy life and my core value has been ignored (hence why I always felt miserable after a binge). Bingeing meant that in the search for living my core value (going out for a drink with friends, or eating yummy food), I'd violated my core value by living it too hard. I had been at war with myself in the search for enjoyment.

How to Make Peace with Your Past?

Food is not actually the problem. It's a solution to a problem. The true problem is the relationship with your emotions and yourself.

The sum total of your beliefs, values, experiences and attitudes toward those experiences are the foundation of where you are today. Your past has led you down your current road, but you have a choice to build a different foundation and choose a different road to travel on.

It's about unbecoming everything and letting go of things that have weighed you down. Maybe the hardest things to let go of are the ones that you need to let go first.

You can't change the past, but you can learn from it and change how you feel about moving forward. If you can't let go, consider why you are holding on so tightly in the first place?

If you had a magic wand, and you could wave it to change anything in your life, what would you want more of? What sort of things and experiences do you feel are missing in your life? How can you get them without having a magic wand?

Maybe the hardest things to let go of are the ones that you need to let go first.

Are you focusing on your past or your future?

Simply realising that bingeing is a HABIT, not a life sentence, was a big moment in our lives and in the lives of so many clients that we have helped. Once we tore off the self-branded label of 'being a binger', we knew we then had the power to change the habit with the skills we're sharing in this book and the choice and persistence to make it happen.

Megan says she got to the stage of just being tired of the whole dieting cycle and was too exhausted to try again. She made the decision that enough was enough, and knew she had to stop dieting. She noticed what foods nourished her body by focusing on her health and wellbeing rather than her size. She surrendered to whatever her weight wanted to be with no rules, no meal plans, no judgements and no effort and relaxed around food. Food was just food. "It was just a habit that kept trying to force me into a smaller size by controlling my food intake and it was a disaster. The only size I was ever going to be was my own size." She learned to recognise when she was genuinely hungry and when she started restricting. She would ask herself, "Why am I not eating? What's going on with me?"

HABITS can be broken.

When you finally come to the decision that you'll do what it takes to set yourself free of the binge monster, it requires patience and perseverance. Be okay with taking it one day and one decision at a time.

When you have disordered thinking around food, you need to separate the thoughts from who you are. You are not your thoughts; you are more than the binge eating.

When Megan accepted, she had to change her habits, she started noticing small changes. Instead of focusing on food, she paid more attention to her feelings. She needed a different way to respond. When she realised how mean and dismissive she had been to herself, she learnt to speak differently. Speaking to herself harshly made her feel bad – and then she stopped eating. She wouldn't talk like that to her friends, so she started talking to herself differently. Would I speak like that to a friend?

You are not your thoughts; you are more than the binge eating.

Your Inner Critic.

Your inner critic is responsible for a lot of the stuff that goes on inside you. Such as your thoughts, how you talk to yourself, how you relate to yourself, your emotions and your needs. As well as how tough you are on yourself.

Where do those harsh and nagging thoughts such as you are fat, lazy, ugly, a terrible person come from? From your inner critic, sometimes it's your own worst enemy. It plays a 'shame game' with you which involves telling you what's wrong with you and making you feel unworthy and incompetent. It's the voice of self-doubt. There is no room for growth, so it keeps us stuck.

You can only silence your inner critic when you are actually aware of it, so try and identify what it's telling you. Make your inner critic separate to you by putting it in the 'second person' (you) and approach it with understanding, compassion and empathy. The first step is separating yourself from this inner critic by:

- Naming it
- Noticing it
- Recognising it

Try giving your inner critic a personality, using an accent to change the way it speaks to you may help. Take even more power away from it by speaking to it out loud. When your inner critic is being judgmental, remember, empathy always win. Stop the self-criticism and start the self-compassion.

Activity.
The Voice.

Here's a fun way to turn your inner critic into a friend. Give your inner-critic binge eating a personality with a name.

Karyn has labelled this inner critic 'Sargent Shultz' from the television show Hogan's Heroes and Megan calls it 'The Freak' (a character from the Australian television show, Prisoner).

Megan says, "Once I identified 'The Freak' I could interact with her every time she spoke to me. She would say "Let's get thinner" and I would reply and say, "No Freak, I'm done with diets. I'm ok, you're ok. I'm good enough, and we don't have to change anything. I can handle the situation."

It didn't take long at all for The Freak to become quiet. This was a complete game changer for me, and although I still overeat every now and then, this technique has given me the power to choose and be the boss in my head.

You can even take this technique to the next level and change the way your character interacts. For example, I now imagine 'The Freak' speaks like Karyn's bumbling Sargent Schultz. When I confront her, I imagine she uses his mumbling accent and says, "I see nothing! I hear nothing! I know nothing!" 'The Freak' knows nothing, and I have the power now.

John's Story.

John was bullied from a young age; he remembers being called fat from as early as eight years old. "I started to obsess about how I looked, so I started to starve myself and then I'd blow out and binge. I did this for years before seeking help."

John used bingeing and starvation to feel in control, "I was abusing laxatives, I exercised obsessively, it was an obsession in the end."

He kept his secret from everyone and, only once he admitted it, did his life turn around. It gave him the power to do something about it. Now he has a healthier relationship with food and can enjoy life without obsessing. He looks in the mirror every day and says out loud, "I'm not perfect but I am okay."

Karyn's Story.

I believe I am the person I am because of what I survived, and I'm grateful for the faith that my mum had in me. I love her strength. I've learnt that I used alcohol, smoking and junk food as a way to suppress the feelings I had when I experienced loss at such an early age. I realised the challenge for me was that I was also old enough when my dad died to understand the loss, but not old enough to have the skills to cope with it.

Those outlets throughout my life allowed me to hide my vulnerability. I took on the identity of the 'strong one'. It was a vicious cycle of hangovers and junk food. It took its toll, expanding my waist and diminishing my self-belief.

The more my waist band expanded, the unhappier I became, and that led to more partying to cover up the pain. I led a life of false happiness.

Over time, I replaced the partying with binge eating. At first, I just thought I liked food too much, but as I worked on myself I realised it was the 'sneaking' of the food, doing it in secret, that revealed it was a much bigger problem.

One of the most helpful things I learned was that it wasn't my fault that I learned to cope that way, but it was my responsibility to learn how to do something about it once I became conscious and wanted to change.

If you struggle with bingeing you need to know it's NOT your fault that the habit started. Your values and your beliefs are the railway tracks of life and your unconscious mind lays those tracks down based on your past experiences. Our reactions to life are based on the meaning we have given things through our experiences, both good and bad.

As a 15-year-old being given the freedom to party with no parental supervision, I felt like I'd been handed every teenager's dream. Woohoo, no rules, right? But now, I want something different for the teenager me. I used therapy to go back in time and help the teenager inside me who didn't learn boundaries or how to cope with loss.

I masked my pain the same way my mother did. PARTY on the outside, pain on the inside.

So, party and pretend I did. I smoked, binge drank and ate junk food. I thought I was in heaven. I thought I was happy. I'm sure I was for a while; in the only way I knew.

What I know now is that the 15-year-old party girl was really asking: What's wrong with me? Why does everyone leave me? Am I worthless? Am I unlovable?

I don't want you to think my mum was a bad mother. I know now Mum was masking her sadness and loneliness behind a face of bravado.

I learnt at an early age that you can hide the pain inside by putting on a brave face. In the following chapters you will discover the truth. You are worthy and you are not alone. It is not your fault and you are deserving of love.

In Chapter 7 we introduce the importance of self-love and acceptance and how you can improve your relationship with yourself and those around you.

Reminder to download your free resources at
www.eatingsecrets.com.au/resources

CHAPTER 7
Self-Love and Acceptance

"You are always with yourself, so you might as well enjoy the company." Diane Von Furstenberg

The Secret Relationship.

Binge eating is just like having a secret affair. Not only are you cheating yourself, but you are also cheating your relationships. And just like secret affairs, binge eating does not bring happiness or solve problems long term. The fall out is tremendous pain. And because it's secret, it adds to your loneliness and your alone-ness.

Food promises you love, joy and happiness, but fails to deliver and instead you feel more alone. Love of self is the only love that can truly make us happy because it's the only love you can control. When you give the power of love to food or anyone else, happiness and inner peace are external to you, they exist in someone or something else. Put your relationship with yourself and your own wellbeing at the forefront of your priority list. Self-care is not selfish; it's fuel. When we are well cared for, we are less drawn to escapist behaviours like binge eating.

The biggest problem with having a secret relationship is the loneliness. How many relationships have you had that look like this? Perhaps it's reflective of the relationship you have with yourself. If food is a 'comforting friend' why are you friends with someone who treats you badly? Why should you accept this treatment from yourself?

"Your relationship with yourself is the blueprint for all the relationships in your life. Alter your relationship with yourself and your other relationships will change accordingly." – Susyn Reeve

Karyn's Story.

I often felt such intense loneliness that food became my friend when I was up late or home alone. It was the only thing I could rely on when I felt I didn't belong. I'd cancel all plans and isolate myself and binge, then feel ashamed that I didn't want people to know what I was up to.

I'd hide all evidence by pushing the wrappers and packaging down into the trash. It was the loneliness that drew me to the personal development field.

Building my support network was the key to start turning my journey around. Just as physical hunger is the signal for us to eat, loneliness is the sign to seek connection.

The most important relationship you will ever have is the one with yourself. How you feel about yourself is the most important thing in your life. So, learn how to show yourself love, respect, honesty, kindness and patience.

How do you improve your relationship with yourself?

Your needs are important, and it's vital that you approach yourself from love not fear. Lack of self-love and self-neglect is often at the root of overeating, dieting and binge eating.

What you have been doing has not worked. Hating yourself has not worked. Hating yourself keeps you trapped.

If you can't feel love for yourself, then start with acceptance. This might seem to be a difficult task, but I bet you are more accepting of other people than you are of yourself. You will never make anyone else happy if you can't make yourself happy. Once you accept yourself, you can fully accept others.

When you approve of and accept yourself, you stop worrying about what everyone else thinks and your confidence improves. No one is competing with you to be you.

No one is competing with you to be you.

Start accepting who you are now and where you have been. If you don't feel willing to accept yourself the way you are now, today, then start with PART of you.

To fully accept yourself, you need to come to terms with those aspects of yourself that you cannot change. There might be a few things you want to change about yourself – don't we all – but accept yourself completely and choose to focus on your positive features and improve your weaknesses. Make emotional peace with yourself and your choices, no matter what they are. You are only human.

Forgive Yourself.

Building a loving relationship with yourself is an important part of healing and changing the habit of bingeing. When you can forgive yourself, you will feel the burden of guilt, shame and blame lift physically and emotionally.

Forgiveness doesn't come easily for most of us. Self-forgiveness needs kindness. Practice being kind to yourself because we are usually our harshest critics.

True forgiveness is a challenge that takes action. It requires a shift of your emotions and a desire for closure. If you hang on to past hurts, you can't forgive.

Relationships with Others.

If an external relationship is unbalanced, it can be another trigger to eat more and surrender to every craving. In order to heal, sometimes difficult decisions need to be made. You might need to walk away from things or people. If you feel closed off to the world or others, it is because you are closed off to you.

Self-care primes us to be the best version of ourselves in our relationships. Self-compassion is necessary for a real, sustained compassion for others.

A common reason for maintaining the secret of binge eating is the fear of being rejected or judged. When you start to become more authentic and learn to accept yourself, it's important to share your vulnerability with others. As this happens you start to see who is on your team and who isn't as accepting of you as you thought. Find people around you who truly accept who you are and are worthy of your experiences. By loving and accepting yourself, you'll soon find out who doesn't return the same energy.

Do you fight for your own health and happiness the way you would fight for your friends and family?

Relationship with Body.

For as long as we can remember, weight and body image were a huge problem for both of us. A mentor had this to say, "Take a look at the things you think you don't like about yourself. You have a choice: you either learn to accept them for what they are, or you change them. It's simple."

Megan remembers, "I was initially horrified and infuriated. I spent the best part of my life hating how I looked – how on earth was

I going to undo all that self-hatred? Actually, it was easy once I realised I had a choice. I now realise that my body is not perfect but it's not all bad either."

Focus on what your body does for you and block out the negativity.

Self-care is daring to love yourself so much that you are willing to put yourself above all and really take care of yourself first. Ignoring your own self-care leads to feelings of resentment, frustration and stress.

Compliment yourself and others on their character. Not body or appearance. Focus on what your body does for you and block out the negativity.

The Secret Despair.

There is an epidemic now of men and women of all different shapes and sizes who 'hate' their body or parts of it. Although we are 'aware' of the manufactured images in the media and social media, we still compare our natural, unedited appearance to that of others whose lives have been shared after editing and whose images have been *photo shopped* to appear natural.

When you compare yourself with others, you will despair. By comparing, we can get triggered to feel consciously and unconsciously 'not good enough'. The way we speak about our body does not ring of acceptance at all. If you find yourself looking at other images and comparing yourself, stop looking. Make a choice to seek out realistic images that promote confidence and focus on who or what helps you feel better about yourself.

Try to notice when you compare yourself to others. Self-care makes us happier – and it feels good. It's a form of control in a crazy world. Stop looking externally.

Honour Your Body.

Be grateful for the body you have. It's the only one you've got, and it keeps you alive! When we accept that our bodies don't represent who we are emotionally, intellectually or socially, our self-esteem no longer depends on our weight, hair colour, skin tone or some other perceived physical imperfection.

Appreciate how your body has been protecting you, accept it as the home you live in. When you truly love and accept your body unconditionally, your body will stop fighting you because your brain will switch the stress triggers off once the war with yourself is over. Your body will eagerly respond to more peaceful messages from your brain too.

Care for your body so that it can care for you. Be your body's best friend. Be aware of the comments that you make about yourself, they will either break you or heal you. Phrases such as, "I am fat and ugly", "I'm not pretty enough", "I'm not thin enough" or "anything enough" simply reinforce "I am not lovable". Don't be a bully to yourself. Be your best friend.

If you were to speak out loud everything that you say to yourself, would those who overhear you think you were being kind or hurtful? Would you speak to a loved one or your best friend, the way you speak to yourself? By speaking to yourself in that manner, you're causing yourself pain and therefore reminding yourself you're not good enough, which only leads to bingeing. It's time to forgive yourself.

Activity.

Write A Letter.

Writing a forgiveness letter to yourself is challenging but ultimately rewarding and empowering. This letter is between you and the part of you that was binge eating.

Write from the perspective of your best friend who has already embraced forgiveness.

The purpose is to jot down whatever comes to mind, so write whatever you feel, uncensored. Be gentle with yourself. Be aware that it may trigger complex emotions, but you have the right to express them and let the ENERGY MOVE THROUGH YOU IN MOTION.

- Be entirely honest with yourself. Do so without judgement and without suppressing your emotions.
- Become more aware of your emotions around negative events/thoughts/behaviour. Feel all the emotions that surface.
- Ask yourself, what happened right before the onslaught of unkind thoughts or binge eating?
- What initial emotions triggered these thoughts or your desire to reach for unhealthy food for comfort?
- What emotions would you be feeling, or issues would you be facing, if you weren't so busy worrying about your body shape?

Dear Self

I am angry with you because ________________________________

I forgive you because ____________________________________

I love you because____

You can download your 'Love Letter to self' by visiting www.eatingsecrets.com.au/resources

Karyn's Letter to herself.

I am angry with myself because I have done it again. I feel like such a loser because I could not resist the chocolate calling my name. I caved in. I'd been going so well and was treating myself with respect by eating well. Then I had a second shitty day and I just seemed to forget that I was empowered, and I gave in. My coach has warned me that once you have released what causes bingeing, you still need to treat the habit itself.

Yesterday the habit took over. I walked into a store and bought two blocks of chocolate. The rebel in me thought, "F*** you. It's too hard to give up my friend, bingeing." So instead of showing anger at the situation, I hurt myself with bingeing. I ate so much it hurt. I literally couldn't move. It was horrible.

I forgive you because you're human and you're still learning. Remember you need to crawl before you can walk. If, as a baby, you gave up the first time you fell you wouldn't have experienced so much in your life. There will be setbacks, but it's like a muscle that needs to strengthen. I believe in you.

I love you because you never give up and you are awesome. You dust yourself off and get back up. You are caring, loving and a good friend. I choose to feel happy and love myself unconditionally and believe that I will succeed.

Mirror Mirror on the wall...who is the fairest one of all?

"Well it certainly wasn't me," says Megan. She used to hate seeing her reflection in a mirror until she started seeing a therapist. The person she saw in the mirror showed her all her flaws – she was too big and too fat, but it was really an internal conflict she was going through. She felt she was simply too much for others and didn't want to burden them with her needs, so she just burdened herself.

She also hated getting her picture taken and would cringe when she saw herself. When she was backpacking, lots of people noticed she would avoid photos. Someone said to her that she was wasting her life criticising her appearance and it was time she could never get back. It doesn't matter how you look in photos, the most important thing about appearing in pictures is that you were there to make the memory in the first place.

Sometimes the questions you need to answer when you look in the mirror, or see a picture of yourself, will be some of the hardest. But you need to answer them if you want to grow. Think about some more self-accepting mantras that you can tell yourself when your 'inner critic' starts picking apart your appearance in photos or when you look in the mirror.

Imagine looking into a mirror or taking a picture of yourself and saying, "I accept you."

What would happen if you were to start accepting rather than hating the way you look? It all starts with taking the time to accept and thank your body and the way you look. Take in the shape of your eyes, your mouth, all your angles and curves and really see what a perfect specimen you are. Confront judgmental or distorted beliefs about your body and replace those thoughts with more accurate and compassionate ones. Truly accept, without judgement, all that you see.

Introduce a moment in everyday to look in the mirror or take a selfie of yourself. Smile. That's how you develop a kinder relationship with yourself and start seeing yourself through other people's eyes and the wonder that you are.

Karyn's Story.

After losing my father to cancer, I saw my mother alter her whole personality from a church-going good housewife to becoming a party gal: smoking, drinking, swearing and always the life of the party. I know now my mother was masking her sadness. I simply mirrored her reactions by squashing my emotions and turning to food (and later partying and cigs) to replace the safety I no longer had and in turn hating myself whenever I looked in the mirror.

I remember the last conversation I had with my mother, but I can't remember if I said I love you when I hung up.

It was something we always said at the end of a conversation, but on this occasion, I was distracted and excited about a new apartment I'd found and can't remember if I said the words.

Later that night I received a phone call from my sister-in-law telling me that my mother had died. I was in shock because there was absolutely no warning, she'd had a sudden heart attack. Even though I was now 30 years old and thought that I'd become immune to loss, I was devastated.

It's been over 20 years now, and I can still be brought to tears talking about my mother. Grief hit me hard. Watching a sad movie can trigger emotion and I can cry like a little girl. I have learned to allow myself to cry for the loss of my mother and even mourn my lost childhood. I have forgiven the scared little girl within for coping with the grief the only way she knew how, by bingeing and so now I can accept and love ME.

Loving and accepting yourself is an important step to ensure healing.

"If you put shame on a Petri dish, it needs three things to grow exponentially: secrecy, silence and judgement. If you put the same amount of shame in a Petri dish and douse it with empathy, it can't survive." – Dr Brene Brown

---

BOOM!

CHAPTER 8
Setting Yourself up for Success

"Once you choose hope, anything's possible." Christopher Reeve

The Secret Dream.

Walt Disney said, "If you can dream it, you can do it. When you believe in a thing, believe in it all the way, implicitly and unquestionably."

Your future can be whatever you want it to be. Choose to overcome adversity and re-write your own book to ensure you have a happy ending.

"If you can dream it, you can do it. When you believe in a thing, believe in it all the way, implicitly and unquestionably."

You might have heard of a story about a girl who was upset because a mean neighbour wanted to hurt someone she loved. The girl got stuck in her own cyclone of fears and emotions. Seeking to escape, she went on a journey and with the help of three friends, overcame adversity and judgement, and dealt with situations and people who were barriers. All the friends connected and banded together to form a community seeking to solve the problems, and along the way they learnt to find their own gifts within.

Somewhere over the rainbow you will find your full potential using these resources and your loving heart, so have courage, find your OZ. It's just a new way of understanding yourself and it's within you .

There is no place like home!!!

What do you want?

Go back to the days of the dreaming child who had a wild and innocent imagination. Can you remember a time when you believed anything was possible? Perhaps you wanted to be a singer or a dancer, a doctor or a movie star. Perhaps it was an astronaut or something else.

As a child you allowed yourself to dream and believe without judgment.

The world was a magical place and you applied all your senses to your dreams. As a child even your games were filled with wonderment and belief. If you poured make-believe tea for the teddy bears it was real to your heart and mind. You surrendered to imagination as reality.

What did you imagine as a child? What did you want for your heart's desire? Can you remember?

It doesn't matter what it was or whether you remember it exactly or not, we want you to simply remember the complete surrender to the game. The absolute certainty you allowed yourself to feel and experience.

That is how magical change happens. When you find the certainty inside you, it can be so.

Use your imagination, your certainty and commitment to act on the techniques we've shared, and your trust in yourself and your willingness to love and accept yourself again. It is time to use that same imagination and emotion to do and be what you want to be and do now!

"There is a superhero in all of us, we just need the courage to put on the cape" – Superman

Imagine you are Clark Kent and you walked into a telephone booth, did a little dance and an abracadabra and walked out of the telephone booth with a big ta-da and you are now Superman. You are now a superhero who has a cape and superpowers to be and do anything you want. You could be binge-free! Imagine if it were just that simple. What cape do you need to put on to be binge-free? What do you need to be your own superhero?

Imagine if you could see the outcome of you binge-free. You are smiling at your own success, with joy and self-acceptance in your eyes. Really immerse yourself in this picture and bring it to life through your senses. Notice how you feel, what you see and what you think or say to yourself and others as you 'play out' your outcomes. Notice who you need to BE and DO to achieve your goal. Hold that photo in your mind and take a deep breath and breathe life into it. Make it appear really alive. Gently release the image and purse your lips to blow it into your future. Blow enough life into the picture that the picture floats towards your dreams.

Who do you want to be?

We have witnessed many people struggling so much with binge eating that they start to over-identify with it. It becomes a part of them. "I am a binge eater." They have spent most of their lives consumed by food either by thinking or talking about it. No matter how much pain it brings them, they are unwilling to let it go. It provides them with a meaning and a purpose. It is something that has been a constant in their lives for such a long time and it has provided them with emotional support – sometimes it has been their only friend. Perhaps you too wear it as a badge of honour? Whatever you do in your life or what you have is a reflection of your identity.

If you have defined yourself in the past as 'someone who binges', re-define and choose a new identity for yourself.

What other ways do you identify yourself?

Do you identify as someone who sabotages their success? Or someone who is determined?

Do you identify as someone who makes up their mind and does it? Or someone who can't follow through?

Activity.

How to rewrite your story.

This re-writing your story exercise gives you a chance to get clear on your new identity of who you need to become so you can react differently to your old bingeing triggers. It's time to step in the telephone booth and make the decision to walk out and become your own superhero.

Rewrite Your Story	
I am a person who thinks…	
I am a person who believes…	
I am a person who likes…	
I am a person who feels…	
I am a person who eats…	
I am a person who treats their body with…	
I am the kind of person who accepts…	
I am…	
I am…	
I am…	
I am…	

You can download your 'Rewrite Your Story' chart by visiting www.eatingsecrets.com.au/resources

Accountability.

Anyone who understands the struggle of binge eating will know how difficult and embarrassing it is to admit. It's also very difficult for people to understand the struggles you are going through if they've never had the same experiences as you. For the longest time we were embarrassed by our story. We're certainly not proud of it, and it was something that we struggled with and kept secret for too long. But we are proud that we faced it and learned how to deal with it.

We both know how beneficial it is to work with a mentor and coach. We made ourselves accountable to others to keep ourselves on track and to heal to the deepest level. So, can you. Anything less is not going to work. If you are struggling and need help, please seek feedback from someone who has walked a similar path to you, to help you stay on course.

Seek professional help when you're ready to decide it's your time. Your strength is in your choice to be vulnerable and ask for help, so you can step out of the comfort zone you've been in for so long. Change comes from making changes. We offer an online course to provide you with the much-needed ongoing support to help you become binge free.

Karyn's Story.

Exercise was not something I loved.

I did it only to achieve weight loss. This meant sticking to it was almost impossible, because it felt like a chore. Imagine being tired and just wanting to go home and sleep or, better still, plan on what I can buy so I can go home and binge. Well that used to be my day.

I found it hard to make a decision to exercise when I was tired and unmotivated. I would then berate myself, saying things like, "You're lazy." Then that inner battle would lead me to a binge. This was a cycle I lived with for many, many years until my coach discovered a belief that was holding me back.

Due to the hurt and pain of death and loss I experienced at a young age; I had created a belief that exercise meant death.

Once that was cleared at an unconscious level, I discovered I really loved the challenge of exercise and even took up running and triathlons.

Working with my coaches has been the most amazing experience. No one wants to feel as if they're doing it alone, and even with all my skills it's hard for me to help myself because I'm too close to my own problem, as we all often are.

My coaches have given me a different perspective and have helped me clear traumas that were keeping me stuck and causing me to self-sabotage.

I have learnt so many valuable lessons and my clients receive these as a bonus when they work with me because they get that wisdom too. Being accountable to my coach also allowed me to stay on the path of my dreams and jump through hurdles that I otherwise would have strayed.

In Chapter 9 Megan and I address one of the big patterns that keep us on the emotional roller coaster – striving for success and then spiraling into self-sabotage. To overcome this formidable challenge, we have a few extra techniques to keep you on track.

YEAH, I CAN DO ONE STEP.

CHAPTER 9
One Small Step

"When I let go of what I am, I become what I might be." Lao Tzu

The Secret Promise.

Do you want a healthier and happier you? At some point you need to decide. We can't decide it for you, we can only be here for you when you decide for yourself.

You only have two options if you want to overcome binge eating and self-sabotaging behaviours for good:

One Day or Day One.

Any day is good, but the reality is there is no valid reason to postpone your life any longer. Once you decide there is no turning back. You only have one life to live. Promise yourself you will choose the day. Why not today?

Sometimes we get so focused on having everything "perfect" that we never get past Day One. But this is a different kind of Day One.

Take One Small Step.

Look at every unfavourable impact that bingeing has had on your life. You can only change if you are willing to stand face to face with the problem, identify it and make the firm decision to change it. Knowing what's holding you back is vital for moving forward. Without appropriate action, you will see little results.

Make the strategies from this book part of your daily routine. We know the journey so well, you will only be able to get the results you need with a new routine (persistence, consistency, patience and faith).

Make sure the steps you take are broken down into small chunks. Just one small achievable change that you can follow through on with certainty, gives you an opportunity to build on from the success. Take one small step but start today.

Recreate a 'love' relationship instead of a 'hate' relationship with food and yourself.

Choose one small change.

The idea is that if you make the steps or changes small enough, you won't fail. Starting small will make new habits because you're more likely to stick with them, allowing them to become new habits. If you want to have a completely different life in a few weeks or months, you need to start now, and you need to start small. By taking small steps, you are taking actions towards your goals.

Don't break your word. If you say you are going to do something to help break the bingeing habit and don't do it, then you are teaching yourself how to not follow through. Make smaller more achievable steps that start giving your brain evidence of success.

Once you can understand your 'why' and you have cleared the path of resistance, you then have to do something to make the required changes. Taking actions towards your goals is the only way to achieve success.

Each week choose one small change you will implement for that week and create your new habits.

Below are some examples of some small steps you can take. Start small and chose one. Maybe stick to that change for a week and gradually add more. You can also create your own list.

Here are some examples

- Keep healthy food around you
- Stop buying your go-to unhealthy snacks so you're not even tempted
- Chew slowly and eat mindfully
- Give up on take away food and start preparing your own meals instead
- Stop drinking sugars – soda/diet soda, and cut back on foods with sugar
- Drink more water
- Pour dishwashing liquid on food and throw it in the bin if it feels like you don't trust yourself not to binge on that food yet
- If large meals are a problem, buy smaller plates
- Address portion size by comparing the size of your portion with your closed fist. Your fist is approximately the size of your stomach. Eat only the portion that when chewed, would equal that fist size
- Serve your dinner and put leftovers immediately into containers for another meal

- If your old 'go-to' is eating mindlessly on the couch or in front of the TV or night-time bingeing – don't eat on the couch
- Squat during TV commercials/pace while you talk on the phone/march in place
- Close the kitchen at night – establish a time when you will stop eating
- Anytime an emotional or habitual craving happens, roll your eyes to the right then to the left and then march on the spot. Most times the craving will diminish.

How to learn from a setback?

Take a breath and switch your focus back to now.

Explore what happened to knock you off track, learn from it, and accept it as progress. Let the E-MOTION go and move on. Make notes on your progress so far and ask yourself, "What can I do differently now? What would you like right now? How can I look after you right now?"

Firstly, forgive yourself. If you do lapse, start over fresh next time you eat – not tomorrow or Monday.

You have identified and peeled away the layers of why and how you binge, so now you are ready to take the actions to ensure you live the life of your dreams. It will only happen if you take the actions by healing your 'stuff' and choosing the habits that need changing.

Perhaps you're 'good' for a little while, but then you start restricting your food and then the binge happens again. You fall off the wagon. Be kind to yourself. Be careful of what you say to yourself. Harsh, critical words will only spin you into another binge and you are likely to continue eating.

Yes, you may feel discouraged and upset with yourself if the wagon gets shaky. Yes, you will feel terrible and adopt a 'don't care' attitude for a short while. But forgive yourself, move on, and choose differently in the next moment.

Count your days of progress, not the times you relapse. Overeating at one meal is not a binge. Be kind to yourself because it is a journey.

Sometimes we get so focused on being perfect that we never get past Day One. It's very important that the only thing you count is the days of progress. It takes just one small action, one small change per day towards your goal.

Make a promise to yourself that you will do one small achievable action every day. And repeat. You need to make it work for you.

"Motivation is what gets you started, habit is what keeps you going."
Jim Rohn

What steps do you need to take to be binge free? You only have one life to live. Choose the Day.

In the next and final Chapter 10 we introduce you to the important act of rewarding yourself and finally saying "See Ya Bingeing" for good

You can download free resources from the book at
www.eatingsecrets.com.au/resources

THE FUTURE LOOKS GOOD.

CHAPTER 10
See Ya Bingeing

"If you are brave enough to say goodbye, life will reward you with a new hello." Paulo Coehlo

Be Your Own Secret Weapon.

By now you should have a better understanding of what's really going on. How it was never about food, that there was always a hidden emotion involved. We seek happiness in food – we eat because we want to change how we feel.

The secret is understanding how you feel and allowing yourself to feel it. Whether that is good or bad. Because when you heal yourself, you won't need to use food to cope.

- **Be Aware**. Address where you are now and acknowledge where you are today, where you eat from a place of intention and not from a reaction.
- **Identify and address** your binge-eating triggers as they will be everywhere but avoiding triggers WILL NOT WORK. You need to learn how to handle them better. When you're triggered, it means there is 'unresolved stuff' still to be looked at. You can't keep sweeping it under the carpet if you want success.

- **Clear out the 'stuff'.** The eating is simply the symptom of your stuff. You need to remove the cause to break free of the habit.
- **Rehearse.** Spend time mentally going out into your future and practice new reactions to old bingeing triggers. **Focus on what you want**, not what you don't want.

Focus on what you want, not what you don't want.

- **Make peace with yourself** and your past and turn your inner critic into a friend. Reduce your stress, be kind to yourself, and give yourself permission. Life dishes out some very stressful situations at the most unexpected times. If your old habits start creeping up on you, pay attention to what thoughts are linked to the triggers and reactions. What emotions come up for you? Write them down.
- **Stop Labelling Yourself and Food.** Be aware of the labels you give yourself. And pay attention to the labels you give food. There are no good or bad foods, simply healthy and unhealthy quantities of everything. So, eliminate your 'no' or 'bad' food list. Stop dieting and skipping meals. Restricting (dieting) leads to stress and obsession for someone with a bingeing history.
- **Make your new rules and develop a contract with yourself and your body.** Make one clear rule and set it in stone. If the task is too overwhelming, focus on one step at a time. Commit and do it every single day, at the same time every day. Small daily changes add up and lead to long term change. Decide and learn how to plan for what you want for tomorrow and act on the steps to put that plan into place.
- **Create New Habits.** It takes time to form a new habit, so stick to one change and do it consistently. When you introduce the new habit, at the same time choose a habit you wish to remove. Then each week choose at least one habit to

introduce and one to remove. Within a month you will have started at least four new habits and removed four habits that no longer serve you.

- **Be proud of yourself** for coming so far. Look back, summarise and celebrate!

Secret to Rewarding Yourself.

It's important to reward yourself as it tells your brain something good has happened and sends out positive emotions. It's also important to make sure rewards are not food related. We have learnt how our bingeing is attached to emotions and how we have used food to squash those emotions, so rewarding with food is only going to attach more unwanted meanings to food. Can you remember being given rewards growing up and can you remember the good feelings attached to the actions you took to receive that reward? You may even find that activity is something you now excel in because of the rewards you achieved.

Rewarding yourself with a non-food reward when you overcome bingeing is important to ensure you continue to alter your patterns. You'll gain the momentum due to your new routines and before you know it you have achieved success.

Activity

Gem Jar.

You can also create your own gem jar. Write on a piece of paper all the non-food rewards that would give you joy and place them in a jar. Every time you enjoy a day binge-free, pull one of your rewards out of the jar and reward yourself. Examples: Get a facial, get a massage, go for a walk, ring a friend, go to the movies, buy a new dress, go to the beach, read a book, get a tattoo, plan a holiday, learn a musical instrument, meditate, listen to music, dance, buy some jewellery.

Say Farewell to Bingeing.

We really encourage closure or a ceremony to let go of behaviours and habits that no longer serve us.

Some clients get closure by burning or ripping up a picture of their eating disorder. We encourage them to find or draw a picture that represents their old eating disorder and burn it (in a safe manner) and then stomp on the ashes. If you think that might work for you, tell your eating disorder that you release it and that it has lost its hold on you because you are in control, confident and healthy. Tell the disorder that you do not claim it anymore.

Another way to say goodbye and to let go is to write a letter and farewell binge eating once and for all.

> Some clients like to write a letter to themselves that gets sent to them at a date in the future. What would your future self say to you today? https://www.futureme.org/

Karyn's Farewell to Bingeing.

I believe the corner has been turned.

I have been in circumstances where bingeing would have been very much an unconscious doing without much thought and if I did think, it would be a, "F*** You! I don't care."

Recently I have been in those same trigger situations and guess what? The monster did not stir. I leave food on my plate once I am comfortably full. I haven't bought chocolate or wanted to.

I've walked down the aisles of the supermarket where old binge food lives and the old thought that lied to me never even popped into my head. It used to say, "I'll just buy some 'healthy' binge-worthy snacks for just in case", but I knew I'd eat them all in one day.

The constant nagging in my head from the monster has been silenced. The combination of healing the past and discovering the unconscious meanings I had attached to food, means that all the shitty beliefs and programs I had been running have been broken.

Is this how other people feel about food? It is nice. It's not earth shattering, there are no big brass bands playing, it is simply peaceful. It feels like I am home in my comfy bed – nothing like sleeping in your own bed, hey.

I realised that food was filling a hole inside me, and no amount of food I ate could make me feel satisfied. Once I made the decision to change my life, and to finally get to the root issues, food no longer has the power over me.

I am finally writing and directing the movie of my life. I have the feel-good happy ending to MY movie at last!

Megan's Farewell to Bingeing.

There were so many layers of 'stuff' that had contributed to my 'dieting', that they took a little time to be uncovered. I developed bad habits and behaviours and beliefs around food, drinking, eating, and myself, so there were a few layers that needed to be un-raveled and there was a lot of work involved. I realised that what I was doing was hurting me far more than helping me.

I now 'move' my body instead of 'exercising', and it is now something I enjoy doing. I am thankful that my body can support me and has taught me how it suffers if it is not taken care of. I thank my old bad habits for giving me insight into many things that weren't working for me in my life, and not looking after myself for getting me to where I am today, because now I know what looking after myself really means.

I'm much more self-aware now. When I look in the mirror these days, I see all the changes I have made in my life. I now focus on creating a fulfilling and meaningful life. I also see fear as well. But I'm aware of my triggers and I am prepared for them. I spent years focusing on how I looked and my weight, but my body was never the problem to begin with. Binge eating forced my weight to plummet and yoyo and took my self-esteem with it. Today, I choose a life which doesn't involve bingeing.

Wishing you every success and every happiness on your journey.

With much love.

Karyn and Megan xx

HOW TO HELP A BINGE EATER

Binge eating only has power because it is most often kept a secret, and the secret brings shame, guilt, isolation and loneliness. The secret thrives on silence and most often, you don't even know how long your loved one may have been suffering. Supporting a loved one will be difficult, and it is important that you also look after yourself in the process.

Many people have struggled and recovered, and recovery is all about finding yourself again. Sometimes it just takes time, tears and lots of love. In fact, as Megan and Karyn pulled the resources for this cheat sheet together, tears flowed as they remembered feeling alone in the secret.

Megan says, *"As Karyn and I pulled this book and cheat sheet together, we realised that this was what we wanted and needed all those years ago."*

Megan: *"It was not just the tools and resources that I needed, but I wanted to know I had someone who really 'got me.' Someone who knew the journey and could support me and have my back."*

With this in mind, Karyn and Megan have supplied this cheat sheet and many of the book's resources as free downloads. www.eatingsecrets.com.au/resources

Karyn: *"We hope that these resources and the fact that we care, we get you, and we will support you or someone you care about too. Just reach out to us and we can have a chat about your needs."*

Remember you can reach out to Megan and Karyn at www.relationshionshifters.com

CHEAT SHEET - The Help You'll Need To download free helpful resources from the book visit www.eatingsecrets.com.au/resources		
YOU	**TIP**	**GUIDANCE**
Educate Yourself.	Binge eating is very misunderstood. It is not a choice.	To support somebody who suffers it's important to educate yourself. When you don't have a problem with food, it's easy to have the 'solution'. You cannot 'fix' their problem on your own, however, you can make a huge difference to them in their recovery. Before bringing up the topic, do your research and educate yourself about the disorder and what it involves, so you can better prepare yourself when you talk to them. They already feel bad about their bodies and any extra weight they are carrying, so don't judge them and be ready to offer encouragement, remembering that people who binge feel very ashamed and very alone.

YOU	TIP	GUIDANCE
Listen to Them.	We all need somebody who we can talk to. Be that person that they can turn to.	You don't have to agree with what they are saying, and you probably won't even understand it. Be a supportive listener and listen without judgement. Let them explain it in their own words. Don't be offended by what you hear and don't take the revelations personally. Let them know you care, and you are ready to listen when they are ready to talk. Listen to them and let them open up about how they feel. Be patient with them.
Talk to Them.	Talk to them about their binge eating in a caring manner and let them know you are concerned about their health.	Let them know they are not alone and that you will support them. Don't criticise how they look or their weight and try and resist the urge to 'fix' them. Don't try and solve their problems with your advice or solutions. Steer clear from disparaging remarks or comments that focus on diet, appearance, body weight, food, size, image etc. You could be making it worse for them. Be non-confrontational and use positive language and avoid comments that will shame them or make them feel guilty.

YOU	TIP	GUIDANCE
Support Them.	They need to feel safe when they finally open up especially in moments where it becomes hard for them.	Be supportive and validate what they are saying. They are still a person who suffers from binge eating. Tell them you believe in them – and mean it. Ask how you can help or assist them and give them all the support you can. Stay connected to them and encourage them to open up.
Seek Professional Help.	They probably feel a lot of shame with their binge eating and perhaps don't yet feel 'sick' enough to get help, however, mention how treatment can help them better manage their symptoms.	Getting help can feel very threatening. Encourage them to seek professional help from an expert who understands the disorder. Consider having therapy yourself to help cope with your own experiences and feelings.

Say to them often – I love you and I care about you.
You are not alone.
Let's do this together.

To download free helpful resources from the book visit
www.eatingsecrets.com.au/resources

ACKNOWLEDGEMENTS

We acknowledge and thank our many clients who've taught us about eating secrets, and the secrets that 'feed' them. This book exists because of the brave and courageous people who shared their hopes and fears and their most secret thoughts with us. We are deeply grateful to all of you.

We especially thank the extraordinary Maggie Wilde and Trish Walker for their loving encouragement and support, for organising us and for sharing our dream and vision of this book and the publishing and editing of this book. You helped us from the start to make it real and put the idea down on paper, and to give us a voice. We are eternally grateful for the opportunity.

We thank all our inspirational mentors and teachers who we've met and learned from along the way. You know who you are, you have been a significant part of our recovery and our journey, as well as the knowledge we have gained from your brilliant education.

We thank our families and dearest friends who surround us with unconditional love and support, and who continue to be a source of inspiration for us.

To download free helpful resources, visit
www.eatingsecrets.com.au/resources

MEET THE CONTRIBUTOR

Maggie Wilde – The Potentialist

Maggie Wilde is a 10-time award-winning Author and Publisher in the categories of Psychology and Mental Health, Women's Health and Wellness, Innovation to the Dieting Industry, Alternative Therapies and Mental and Emotional Wellness.

Maggie is the director and founder of Mind Potential Publishing and is an internationally accredited Clinical Therapist. She is the creator of a unique 3-Step Brain Training Model, developed while she recovered from a stroke at the age of 39. Her Brain Training Model is now embraced by other therapists and clients throughout the world.

As a Publisher and author to the Wellness Industry, Maggie now helps other Practitioners share their message to a global audience by publishing their books and online programs.

www.thepotentialist.com

www.facebook.com/maggiewildeauthor

MEET THE AUTHORS

Megan Harris

Karyn de Mol

Both Megan and Karyn have lived through tumultuous battles with binge eating and weight challenges. They both understand the depth of courage, focus and strength required to take charge of these habits. As therapists and coaches, they now help others do the same.

Their group courses and online programs reach a global audience, and they continue to coach clients individually and in small groups to overcome their battles with food, weight and body image. By popular demand, they now share their tried and tested strategies and solutions through their books and online course.

Megan's struggle began in her teens with her main issues being body image and her relationship with food. She believed she had to be thin to be accepted, so she starved herself in order to live up to the world's standards. Her obsession with dieting (starvation eating), and body image, led to a desire to understand herself better, especially why her habits had become so out of control. For many years she over-exercised and ate very little, then she would reward herself with copious amounts of wine. She was convinced that if she just found the perfect diet, or reached a certain goal weight or clothing size, then her problems would go away. The cycle continued until her mid to late 20s when she fell in love with her life and took the pressure off herself and her body. She realised there was more to her than a size 10 pair of jeans.

As an accountant, Megan is trained to organise and balance numbers to work in the best interest for business success. In her transitional training using therapeutic modalities, Megan realised that organising the mind and your habits to work for you rather than against you, was all about balance too. She now loves helping women overcome their body image and eating challenges.

Megan has a Dip. Clin Hypnotherapy, Adv Dip Hypnotherapy, Adv Dip Hypnosis, Dip. Modern Psychology, Master Practitioner NLP and Time Line Therapy, Master Practitioner of Positive Psychology & EQ Facilitator, Certified Practitioner EFT (Emotional Freedom Techniques) and Energy Psychology. Qualified Life Coach.

To download free helpful resources, visit
www.eatingsecrets.com.au/resources

www.relationshifters.com

Karyn struggled with her weight since her teenage years. She thought she didn't belong because her friends all had a 'normal' shape and size. She learned from an early age that food made you 'feel good' and food meant 'love.' Family gatherings were all focused on food and connection. When she was 10 years old her father died. Karyn used food as the solution to resolve her loneliness and grief, as did her mother.

Today Karyn is also a successful accountant with a burning desire to find balance not only on the balance sheet, but on the inside too. Karyn has spent years dedicated to learning therapeutic modalities that have helped her find who she is on the inside, rather than only what she and people saw on the outside. Karyn has found her passion and has transitioned to work with women to empower them to love and accept themselves and overcome the beliefs that hold them back from finding balance in life and feeling peace in their heart and mind.

Karyn has an Adv Dip Hypnotherapy and is a NLP, Hypnosis trainer, Master Practitioner of Time Line Therapy and NLP, Master Practitioner of Positive Psychology & EQ Facilitator. She is a Neuro Linguistic Programming Coach, Reiki Master and a Creatrix® Transformologist®, Certified Practitioner in Specialised Kinesiology and Touch for Health, goal setting and health metaphors for Kinesiology, Certified Practitioner in EFT (Emotional Freedom Techniques), Energy Psychology.

WHAT OTHERS HAVE TO SAY

"I came to Megan based on a recommendation from a close friend who also struggles with weight and binge eating. She had such a successful result that I felt I had nothing to lose. It was the most amazing experience of my life. I noticed a change in the way I think about myself and my relationship with food. I cannot thank her enough for helping me come to the realisations that I often doubted that I would ever have. I can't recommend her or hypnotherapy enough!" **Joanne H**

"Thanks Karyn! You will be pleased to hear that I have not touched one red frog let alone a bagful!!! I have hung up a new dress for my sister's 50th birthday in a few months. Very relaxing at bedtime to listen to your recording. It's a big step for me in the right direction. Thank you!" **Alison A**

"I made an appointment with Megan after seeing other coaches who just didn't provide me with any support or guidance that I felt I needed. After the session and within a few days I noticed that I was making significant progress and finally felt I was making progress in the direction I needed to go. The session was very comfortable, she was very friendly and I' m looking forward to the next stage." **Theresa S**

"I'm feeling good and surprised about how full I'm feeling after eating smaller amounts. I'm feeling positive! Thank you Karyn!" **Robin W**

"Megan helped me to really find out what was making me unhappy beyond the weight. I have tried so many things and this is the first time I feel like I am doing the real work. What I found was me – the real me – not the me with extra kilos, but the me that has been dying to 'break out' and be free. As a result, I'm more than ready to take bigger risks, I found a new partner and am starting to actually live the moment I actually wanted. I wish I had embarked on 'the journey' years go." **Sharon P**

"Karyn's advice to me has always been from the heart, intuitive, gentle, kind and encouraging. Karyn is the most selfless person I know – injecting so much of her personal energy into helping me live a more fulfilled life. Constant information to expand my knowledge on the link of good food choices and the impact on our health. I will be forever grateful to her. I am now more energised than I have been in years, no longer having iron infusions and well and truly onto the journey of understanding how our food is linked to our health.

My only regret is that I had not met Karyn years ago when I was a young mum, struggling to keep up with the energy of our two children. Relying on high levels of caffeine in order to be able to push through the days."

Angie B

"The book is real, and it is honest, it is funny and inspiring. The authors get you; they've heard your secrets whispered inside their heads.

In this ground-breaking and inspiring book, Megan and Karyn help the reader understand that it's not their fault they've developed this love/hate/shame relationship with food, and for some, their body too. The book is real, and it is honest, it is funny and inspiring. The authors get you; they've heard your secrets whispered inside their heads." - **Maggie Wilde - The Potentialist**

"Wow so for all these years I thought that there was something wrong with me....... thank you, Karyn & Megan, for putting things into perspective for me. Your book is so empowering...... a fantastic read, hard to put down." - **Joanne K**

"I would recommend this book to anyone who struggles with emotional eating. Karyn and Megan's personal journeys are both honest and inspiring, and this book is full of simple, practical strategies for a healthier relationship with food." – **Caroline S**

"I found it hard to put the book down, I read it all in one go. I related so well to the secrets in the book, that I felt 'normal' and less alone for the first time in a long time. The authors are true to their word they do 'get you'. Congratulations on your book." – **Matthew C**

"Once I started reading, I couldn't book this book down. I had so many a-ha moments when it came to my own relationships with food, alcohol and cigarettes. I realised that my 'secrets' were causing me to 'feed' my shame and loneliness. Thank you for writing this book! It's helped find a piece of a jigsaw puzzle I didn't know I was looking for!" – **Natalie D**

"I had a gastric band operation many years ago and even that didn't stop me from bingeing. I'd binge until I ended up in hospital. My biggest regret is that I wasn't helped more with why I was bingeing in the first place. Great book and some very powerful insights." – **Donna F**

"A must read for anyone struggling with or worrying about their weight. As a busy single mum, running my own business and studying I often find myself snacking and not eating properly, constantly starting a new eating plan and falling back into unhealthy patterns. I never associated my eating patterns to bingeing. I felt like these 2 amazing ladies had written this book especially for me. It's honest, confronting, funny, educational and inspirational.... thank you!" - **Airlie M**

"Thanks for the privilege of reading your book before publication. Very thoughtful reading, quite a lot to relate to. You are very brave to bare your soul." - **Kim T**

"OMG. I feel like you are in my head, I've already laughed and cried and I'm at page 22! I need to sleep as I'm so tired but can't put it down. Ok so I finished the book this morning! All I can say is WOW... this has opened my eye, to what I have been dealing with my entire grown up life! For the first time in my adult life, I have realised that I am a binge eater & I have a problem! I'm so overwhelmed! Once I have had a chance to clear my head, I'm going to re-read it and use your techniques to start making changes to my life! I know with your book I believe I can, and I will!" - **Courtney E**

"I'm at the end of the book and really enjoying it. I think it's amazing and I can definitely relate to both of you in certain ways when I have a triggered emotion. Although a lot of times I just don't eat at all especially if I have anxiety, and then other times I stuff my face with chocolate and can't stop. I think so many people have this problem, and it isn't spoken about enough. Especially what the trigger is and digging deep to find what the problem truly is. I really hope the book is successful." **Elise Q**

"I have just finished reading the book and it has blown me away. The open and honest re-telling of the authors' stories immediately invites you to receive their advice. They remind you that we are all imperfect and that is OK.

We are constantly being shown images of peoples' perfect lives on TV and on Social Media. This inevitably leaves us feeling that we are not good enough. We can become hypercritical of ourselves which is very damaging emotionally. The issue of using food to comfort ourselves and to deal with pain, anxiety, anger, frustration etc.....is so relatable and so many of us do it, yet it is very rarely talked about so openly. This book not only shines a light on the underlying causes of binge eating, but is a practical guide, with tips and solutions, to overcome this pattern of behaviour.

As a Naturopath I am always looking for ways to help people become healthier without going on strict diets or elimination protocols. They do not work in the long term. The best way to eat healthy, is to have a healthy attitude to food. I will certainly be recommending this book as part of that strategy."

Heidi Cummins Naturopath - www.heidicummins.com.au

Download free resources to help you on your journey at
www.eatingsecrets.com.au/resources

Printed in Australia
AUHW020902090821
350051AU00002B/2

9 781922 380180